Close Reading

Grade 6

EMC School

PART OF CARNEGIE LEARNING

PITTSBURGH, PA — ST. PAUL, MN

Close Reading, Grade 6

ISBN 978-1-53384-162-9

©2020 by Carnegie Learning, Inc.
875 Montreal Way
St. Paul, MN 55102
E-mail: info@carnegielearning.com
Web site: www.emcschool.com

Printed in the United States of America

27 26 25 24 23 22 21 20 19   3 4 5 6 7 8 9 10

CONTENTS

Introduction   v

Unit 1: Fiction Connections
Fiction Close Reading Model   vi
- SHORT STORY **Lob's Girl**, Joan Aiken   1
- SHORT STORY **The Goodness of Matt Kaizer**, Avi   15
- SHORT STORY **The Circuit**, Francisco Jiménez   29

Unit 2: Fiction Connections
- SHORT STORY **Tuesday of the Other June**, Norma Fox Mazer   37
- SHORT STORY **The Bracelet**, Yoshiko Uchida   49

Unit 3: Nonfiction Connections
Nonfiction Close Reading Model   57
- MEMOIR **The Jacket**, Gary Soto   58
- BIOGRAPHY **Abd al-Rahman Ibrahima**, Walter Dean Myers   64
- PERSONAL ESSAY **Why?**, Anne Frank   77
- ARGUMENTATIVE ESSAY *from* **All I Really Need to Know I Learned in Kindergarten**, Robert Fulghum   81

Unit 4: Nonfiction Connections
- SCIENTIFIC ARTICLE **The Five "Wanderers" of the Ancient Skies**, Dennis Brindell Fradin   85
- DIAGRAM **Noise Levels**, Bob Ludlow   92
  - INFORMATIONAL TEXT CONNECTION Text-to-Text
- MAGAZINE ARTICLE **Hearing Under Siege**, Bob Ludlow   95

Unit 5: Poetry Connections
Poetry Close Reading Model   99
- NARRATIVE POEM **Ode to La Tortilla**, Gary Soto   100
- LYRIC POEM **Abuelito Who**, Sandra Cisneros   104
- LYRIC POEM **Life Doesn't Frighten Me**, Maya Angelou   108
- NARRATIVE POEM **The Walrus and the Carpenter**, Lewis Carroll   112

Unit 6: Poetry Connections
- LYRIC POEM **The Dream Keeper**, Langston Hughes   118
- LYRIC POEM **in Just-**, E. E. Cummings   121

Unit 7: Drama Connections
Drama Close Reading Model   124
- DRAMA **In the Fog**, Milton Geiger   125

Unit 8: Folk Literature Connections
Folk Literature Close Reading Model   136
- GREEK MYTH **Arachne**, Anonymous Retold by Olivia Coolidge   137
- FOLK TALE **Why Monkeys Live in Trees**, Anonymous, Retold by Julius Lester   143

= Close Reading Video in Passport

INTRODUCTION TO CLOSE READING

Practicing the close reading process will help you develop the ability to read complex texts independently and proficiently. And you will be able to apply these reading skills to texts across subject areas, such as science or even math, to become a successful reader in all of your classes.

The *Mirrors & Windows* Close Reading Models at the beginning of each unit walk you through applying the close reading process to fiction, nonfiction, poetry, drama, folk literature, and speeches. The *Close Reading* workbook provides students the opportunity to interact with the models by taking notes, marking the text, and completing graphic organizers.

In the Explore section of Passport, Close Reading Videos provide a step-by-step guided demonstration of the Close Reading Process applied directly to the models from your textbook. The selections with accompanying Close Reading Videos are indicated in the Contents with ⚫.

The Close Reading Process

Close reading means to uncover layers of meaning in a text that lead to a deep comprehension. It's an intensive analysis of a text to discover what it says, how it says it, and what it means. Close reading a text involves careful and repeated readings to uncover the layers of meaning.

FIRST READING **Key Ideas and Details**

During the First Reading you are concerned with *what* the text says. You are asking the questions "What is this about, and how do I know? What can I learn from reading this text? Read to find out what the text is about and what the author's purpose might be for writing it.

SECOND READING **Craft and Structure**

During the Second Reading you are trying to understand *how* the text says it. You are asking "How do the author's writing style, word choices, and text structure help me understand what he or she is saying?"

THIRD READING **Integration of Knowledge and Ideas**

And during the Third Reading you go deeper to understand what it *means*. You are asking "What does this text cause me to think or wonder about some larger aspect of the text and the human condition?"

Fiction Close Reading Model

FIRST READING Key Ideas and Details – What the text says

Build Background

You need to apply two types of background to read fiction effectively. One type is the story's literary and historical context. The other type of background is the personal knowledge and experience you bring to your reading.

Set Purpose

A fiction writer presents characters and actions to say something about life. Set your purpose for reading by asking yourself questions about what you want to get out of the story and what you'd like to know more about.

Make Connections

Notice where connections can be made between the story and your life or the world outside the story. What feelings or thoughts do you have while reading the story?

Use Reading Skills

Apply skills such as determining author's purpose, making inferences, and finding the main idea. Identify a graphic organizer that will help you apply the skill before and while you read. Make predictions about what will happen in the story and confirm or adjust your predictions as you read.

SECOND READING Craft and Structure – How the text says it

Use Text Organization

Determine the structure of the text and how it is organized.

- Break the text down or "chunk" the text into smaller sections to check your comprehension.
- Stop at the end of paragraphs or sections to summarize what you have read.
- When understanding breaks down, reread any difficult parts to increase comprehension.

Analyze Literature

A fiction writer uses literary techniques, such as plot and setting, to create meaning. During the second reading, ask yourself questions such as: What literary elements stand out? Are the characters vivid and interesting? Is there a strong central conflict? As you read, consider how these elements affect your enjoyment and understanding of the story.

Unpack Language

What is the effect of the author's vocabulary and the language choices he or she makes? Make sure to use margin definitions, footnotes, and context clues that give hints to the meaning.

THIRD READING Integration of Knowledge and Ideas – What the text means

Find Meaning

Reread to recall the important details of the story, such as the sequence of events and characters' names. Use this information to interpret, or explain, the meaning of the story.

Make Judgments

Analyze the text by examining details and deciding what they contribute to the meaning. Evaluate the text by making judgments about how the author creates meaning. Ask yourself questions about the text to make sure you're understanding the author's message.

Analyze Literature

Review how the use of literary elements increases your understanding of the story. For example, if the author uses dialogue, how does it help to shape the story's meaning?

Extend Understanding

Synthesize information from the text to create new understanding. Go beyond the text by applying the story's ideas to your own life and exploring further through writing, discussion, or other collaborative projects.

Unit 1

Lob's Girl page 7

SHORT STORY by Joan Aiken

Build Background

Literary Context "Lob's Girl" blends realistic characters and places with mysterious and unexplainable events. The mysterious or ghostly qualities of the story belong to the genre that is sometimes called supernatural fiction. In supernatural fiction, the writer suggests forces or events that are not possible in the real world.

Reader's Context Think of an extraordinary pet or other animal you have known or read about. What could the animal do that seemed nearly human or even superhuman?

_____

_____

Set Purpose

Preview the title and the first paragraph. Predict who Lob is, how he comes to the family, and who Lob's girl is. Confirm or revise your predictions as you read.

Use Reading Skills

Draw Conclusions When you draw conclusions, you make reasonable guesses based on evidence. Create a chart to record significant details from the story and determine what they mean. Put details from the text in the first column and your conclusions in the second column.

Story Details	My Conclusions
Sandy loves playing with Lob.	She will be sad when Lob has to leave.

de•ci•sive•ly (di sī´ siv lē) *adv.*, in a manner not open to question

Use Reading Skills
Draw Conclusions Which character is most likely to be the "girl" of the title? How do you know?

A Short Story by Joan Aiken

Lob's Girl

1 Some people choose their dogs, and some dogs choose their people. The Pengelly family had no say in the choosing of Lob; he came to them in the second way, and very decisively.

2 It began on the beach, the summer when Sandy was five, Don, her older brother, twelve, and the twins were three. Sandy was really Alexandra, because her grandmother had a beautiful picture of a queen in a diamond tiara and high collar of pearls. It hung by Granny Pearce's kitchen sink and was as familiar as the doormat. When Sandy was born everyone agreed that she was the living spit of the picture, and so she was called Alexandra and Sandy for short. On this summer day she was lying peacefully reading a comic and not keeping an eye on the twins, who didn't need it because they were occupied in seeing which of them could wrap the most seaweed around the other one's legs. Father—Bert Pengelly— and Don were up on the Hard[1] painting the bottom boards of the boat in which Father went fishing for pilchards.[2] And Mother—Jean Pengelly—was getting ahead with making the Christmas puddings because she never felt easy in her mind if they weren't made and safely put away by the end of August. As usual, each member of the family was happily getting on with his or her own affairs. Little did they guess how soon this state of things would be changed by the large new member who was going to erupt[3] into their midst.

3 Sandy rolled onto her back to make sure that the twins were not climbing on slippery rocks or getting cut off by the tide. At the same moment a large body struck her forcibly in the midriff,[4] and she was covered by flying sand. Instinctively[5] she shut her eyes and felt the sand being wiped off her face by something that seemed like a warm, rough, damp flannel. She opened her eyes and looked. It was a tongue. Its owner was a large and bouncy young Alsatian, or German shepherd, with topaz[6] eyes, black-tipped prick ears, a thick, soft coat, and a bushy black-tipped tail.

---

1. **the** Hard. Firm part of a beach over which the tide usually does not wash
2. **pilchards.** Fish in the herring family
3. **erupt.** Burst or explode
4. **midriff.** Middle part of the torso
5. **instinctively.** Acting on or according to an inner knowledge or sense
6. **topaz.** Bright yellow-gold in color

4   "*Lob!*" shouted a man farther up the beach. "Lob, come here!" But Lob, as if trying to <u>atone</u> for the surprise he had given her, went on licking the sand off Sandy's face, wagging his tail so hard while he kept on knocking up more clouds of sand. His owner, a gray-haired man with a limp, walked over as quickly as he could and seized him by the collar.

5   "I hope he didn't give you a fright?"[7] the man said to Sandy. "He meant it in play—he's only young."

6   "Oh, no, I think he's *beautiful,*" said Sandy truly. She picked up a bit of driftwood and threw it. Lob, whisking easily out of his master's grip, was after it like a sand-colored bullet. He came back with the stick, beaming, and gave it to Sandy. At the same time he gave himself, though no one else was aware of this at the time. But with Sandy, too, it was love at first sight, and when, after a lot more stick-throwing, she and the twins joined Father and Don to go home for tea, they cast many a backward glance at Lob being led firmly away by his master.

7   "I wish we could play with him every day," Tess sighed.

8   "Why can't we?" said Tim.

9   Sandy explained. "Because Mr. Dodsworth, who owns him, is from Liverpool, and he is only staying at the Fisherman's Arms till Saturday."

10   "Is Liverpool a long way off?"

11   "Right at the other end of England from Cornwall,[8] I'm afraid."

12   It was a Cornish fishing village where the Pengelly family lived, with rocks and cliffs and a strip of beach and a little round harbor, and palm trees growing in the gardens of the little whitewashed stone houses. The village was approached by a narrow, steep, twisting hillroad and guarded by a notice that said LOW GEAR FOR 1 1/2 MILES, DANGEROUS TO CYCLISTS.

13   The Pengelly children went home to scones with Cornish cream and jam,[9] thinking they had seen the last of Lob. But they were much mistaken. The whole family was playing cards by the fire in the front room after supper when there was a loud thump and a crash of china in the kitchen.

14   "My Christmas puddings!" exclaimed Jean, and ran out.

15   "Did you put TNT[10] in them, then?" her husband said.

a·tone (ə tōn´) *v.*, make up for a wrong action

FIRST READ

Use Reading Skills
Clarify What does the author compare Lob to?

SECOND READ

Analyze Literature
Plot What is the conflict in the plot at this point?

---

   7. give you a fright. British way of saying "frighten you"
   8. Cornwall. County at the southwest tip of England
   9. scones with Cornish cream and jam. Typical small meal taken at teatime in Cornwall
  10. TNT. Substance used to make an explosion

16   But it was Lob, who, finding the front door shut, had gone around to the back and bounced in through the open kitchen window, where the puddings were cooling on the sill. Luckily only the smallest was knocked down and broken.

17   Lob stood on his hind legs and plastered Sandy's face with licks. Then he did the same for the twins, who shrieked with joy.

18   "Where does this friend of yours come from?" inquired Mr. Pengelly.

19   "He's staying at the Fisherman's Arms—I mean his owner is."

20   "Then he must go back there. Find a bit of string, Sandy, to tie to his collar."

21   "I wonder how he found his way here," Mrs. Pengelly said, when the reluctant Lob had been led whining away and Sandy had explained about their afternoon's game on the beach. "Fisherman's Arms is right round the other side of the harbor."

22   Lob's owner scolded him and thanked Mr. Pengelly for bringing him back. Jean Pengelly warned the children that they had better not encourage Lob any more if they met him on the beach, or it would only lead to more trouble. So they dutifully took no notice of him the next day until he spoiled their good resolutions[11] by dashing up to them with joyful barks, wagging his tail so hard that he winded Tess and knocked Tim's legs from under him.

23   They had a happy day, playing on the sand.

24   The next day was Saturday. Sandy had found out that Mr. Dodsworth was to catch the half-past-nine train. She went out secretly, down to the station, nodded to Mr. Hoskins, the stationmaster, who wouldn't dream of charging any local for a platform ticket, and climbed up on the footbridge that led over the tracks. She didn't want to be seen, but she did want to see. She saw Mr. Dodsworth get on the train, accompanied by an unhappy-looking Lob with drooping ears and tail. Then she saw the train slide away out of sight around the next headland, with a <u>melancholy</u> wail that sounded like Lob's last good-bye.

25   Sandy wished she hadn't had the idea of coming to the station. She walked home miserably, with her shoulders hunched and her hands in her pockets. For the rest of the day,

SECOND READ ➤

Use Reading Skills
Draw Conclusions What do you think it means that Lob traveled all the way to the Pengelly's alone?

mel•an•cho•ly
(me´ lən kä' lē) *adj.*, sad; gloomy

FIRST READ ➤

Use Reading Skills
Make Predictions What do you think will happen next?

---

11. **resolutions.** Firm or formal decisions often based on earlier opposite behavior

Close Reading

she was so cross and unlike herself that Tess and Tim were quite surprised, and her mother gave her a dose of senna.[12]

26   A week passed. Then, one evening, Mrs. Pengelly and the younger children were in the front room playing snakes and ladders. Mr. Pengelly and Don had gone fishing on the evening tide. If your father is a fisherman, he will never be home at the same time from one week to the next.

27   Suddenly, history repeating itself, there was a crash from the kitchen. Jean Pengelly leaped up, crying, "My blackberry jelly!" She and the children had spent the morning picking and the afternoon boiling fruit.

28   But Sandy was ahead of her mother. With flushed cheeks and eyes like stars she had darted into the kitchen, where she and Lob were hugging one another in a frenzy of joy. About a yard of his tongue was out, and he was licking every part of her that he could reach.

29   "Good heavens!" exclaimed Jean. "How in the world did *he* get here?"

30   "He must have walked," said Sandy. "Look at his feet."

31   They were worn, dusty, and tarry. One had a cut on the pad.

32   "They ought to be bathed," said Jean Pengelly. "Sandy, run a bowl of warm water while I get the disinfectant."

33   "What'll we do about him, Mother?" said Sandy anxiously.

34   Mrs. Pengelly looked at her daughter's pleading eyes and sighed.

35   "He must go back to his owner, of course," she said, making her voice firm. "Your dad can get the address from the

FIRST READ

Make Connections
Have you ever been reunited with a friend or pet after a long separation? How did you feel?

12. **senna.** Herbal cure

Fisherman's tomorrow, and phone him or send a telegram. In the meantime he'd better have a long drink and a good meal."

36   Lob was very grateful for the drink and the meal, and made no objection to having his feet washed. Then he flopped down on the hearth rug and slept in front of the fire they had lit because it was a cold, wet evening, with his head on Sandy's feet. He was a very tired dog. He had walked all the way from Liverpool to Cornwall, which is more than four hundred miles.

37   The next day Mr. Pengelly phoned Lob's owner, and the following morning Mr. Dodsworth arrived off the night train, decidedly put out, to take his pet home. That parting was worse than the first. Lob whined, Don walked out of the house, the twins burst out crying, and Sandy crept up to her bedroom afterward and lay with her face pressed into the quilt, feeling as if she were bruised all over.

38   Jean Pengelly took them all into Plymouth to see the circus on the next day and the twins cheered up a little, but even the hour's ride in the train each way and the Liberty horses and performing seals could not cure Sandy's sore heart.

39   She need not have bothered, though. In ten days' time Lob was back—limping this time, with a torn ear and a patch missing out of his furry coat, as if he had met and tangled with an enemy or two in the course of his four-hundred-mile walk.

40   Bert Pengelly rang up[13] Liverpool again. Mr. Dodsworth, when he answered, sounded weary. He said, "That dog has already cost me two days that I can't spare away from my work—plus endless time in police stations and drafting newspaper advertisements. I'm too old for these ups and downs. I think we'd better face the fact, Mr. Pengelly, that it's your family he wants to stay with—that is, if you want to have him."

41   Bert Pengelly gulped. He was not a rich man, and Lob was a pedigreed dog. He said cautiously, "How much would you be asking for him?"

42   "Good heavens, man, I'm not suggesting I'd *sell* him to you. You must have him as a gift. Think of the train fares I'll be saving. You'll be doing me a good turn."

43   "Is he a big eater?" Bert asked doubtfully.

44   By this time the children, breathless in the background listening to one side of this conversation, had realized what

Use Reading Skills
Ask Questions Why does Bert ask how much Lob eats?

---

13. rang up. British expression for "telephoned"

Close Reading

was in the wind and were dancing up and down with their hands clasped beseechingly.[14]

45   "Oh, not for his size," Lob's owner assured Bert. "Two or three pounds of meat a day and some vegetables and gravy and biscuits—he does very well on that."

46   Alexandra's father looked over the telephone at his daughter's swimming eyes and trembling lips. He reached a decision. "Well, then, Mr. Dodsworth," he said briskly, "we'll accept your offer and thank you very much. The children will be overjoyed and you can be sure Lob has come to a good home. They'll look after him and see he gets enough exercise. But I can tell you," he ended firmly, "if he wants to settle in with us he'll have to learn to eat a lot of fish."

47   So that was how Lob came to live with the Pengelly family. Everybody loved him and he loved them all. But there was never any question who came first with him. He was Sandy's dog. He slept by her bed and followed her everywhere he was allowed.

48   Nine years went by, and each summer Mr. Dodsworth came back to stay at the Fisherman's Arms and call on his erstwhile[15] dog. Lob always met him with recognition and dignified pleasure, accompanied him for a walk or two—but showed no signs of wishing to return to Liverpool. His place, he intimated,[16] was definitely with the Pengellys.

49   In the course of nine years Lob changed less than Sandy. As she went into her teens he became a little slower, a little stiffer, there was a touch of gray on his nose, but he was still a handsome dog. He and Sandy still loved one another devotedly.

50   One evening in October all the summer visitors had left, and the little fishing town looked empty and secretive. It was a wet, windy dusk. When the children came home from school—even the twins were at high school now, and Don was a full-fledged[17] fisherman—Jean Pengelly said, "Sandy, your Aunt Rebecca says she's lonesome because Uncle Will Hoskins has gone out trawling,[18] and she wants one of you to go and spend the evening with her. You go, dear; you can take your homework with you."

51   Sandy looked far from enthusiastic.

52   "Can I take Lob with me?"

---

14. **beseechingly.** Pleadingly
15. **erstwhile.** Previous, former
16. **intimated.** Implied; communicated without saying
17. **full-fledged.** Fully capable
18. **trawling.** Fishing by dragging a net

Close Reading

NOTES

FIRST READ

Use Reading Skills
Visualize Imagine what Bert sees as he looks at his daughter and makes his decision. What do you learn about him at this moment?

SECOND READ

Analyze Literature
Plot Do you think the initial conflict has been resolved now that nine years have passed? Why or why not?

53 "You know Aunt Becky doesn't really like dogs—Oh, very well." Mrs. Pengelly sighed. "I supposed she'll have to put up with him as well as you."

54 Reluctantly Sandy tidied herself, took her schoolbag, put on the damp raincoat she had just taken off, fastened Lob's lead to his collar, and set off to walk through the dusk to Aunt Becky's cottage, which was five minutes' climb up the steep hill.

55 The wind was howling through the shrouds[19] of boats drawn up on the Hard.

56 "Put some cheerful music on, do," said Jean Pengelly to the nearest twin. "Anything to drown that wretched sound while I make your dad's supper." So Don, who had just come in, put on some rock music, loud. Which was why the Pengellys did not hear the truck hurtle[20] down the hill and

57 crash against the post office wall a few minutes later.

Dr. Travers was driving through Cornwall with his wife, taking a late holiday before patients began coming down with the winter colds and flu. He saw the sign that said STEEP HILL. LOW GEAR FOR 1 1/2 MILES. Dutifully he changed

58 into second gear.

"We must be nearly there," said his wife, looking out of her window. "I noticed a sign on the coast road that said the Fisherman's Arms was two miles. What a narrow, dangerous hill! But the cottages are very pretty—Oh, Frank, stop, *stop!*

59 There's a child, I'm sure it's a child—by the wall over there!"

Dr. Travers jammed on his brakes and brought the car to a stop. A little stream ran down by the road in a shallow stone culvert,[21] and half in the water lay something that looked, in the dusk, like a pile of clothes—or was it the body of a child? Mrs. Travers was out of the car in a flash, but her husband was

60 quicker.

"Don't touch her, Emily!" he said sharply. "She's been hit. Can't be more than a few minutes. Remember that truck that overtook us half a mile back, speeding like the devil? Here, quick, go into that cottage and phone for an ambulance. The girl's in a bad way. I'll stay here and do what I can to stop the

61 bleeding. Don't waste a minute."

Doctors are expert at stopping dangerous bleeding, for they know the right places to press. This Dr. Travers was able to do, but he didn't dare do more; the girl was lying in a queerly

FIRST READ

Use Reading Skills
Draw Conclusions Who is the injured child? What makes you think so?

SECOND READ

Analyze Literature
Plot The narrator switches to a different point of view in the paragraphs about the Travers family. How does this change contribute to the plot?

---

19. shrouds. Ropes that help hold up the masts of a boat
20. hurtle. Move rapidly
21. culvert. Drain; a pipe for wastewater below the ground

Close Reading

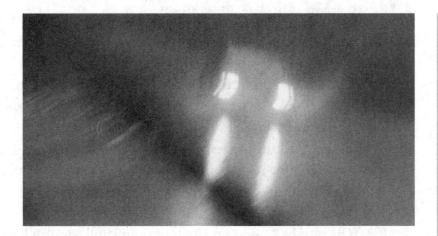

crumpled heap, and he guessed she had a number of bones broken and that it would be highly dangerous to move her. He watched her with great concentration, wondering where the truck had got to and what other damage it had done.

Mrs. Travers was very quick. She had seen plenty of accident cases and knew the importance of speed. The first cottage she tried had a phone; in four minutes she was back, and in six an ambulance was wailing down the hill.

Its attendants lifted the child onto a stretcher as carefully as if she were made of fine thistledown. The ambulance sped off to Plymouth—for the local cottage hospital did not take serious accident cases—and Dr. Travers went down to the police station to report what he had done.

He found that the police already knew about the speeding truck—which had suffered from loss of brakes and ended up with its radiator halfway through the post-office wall. The driver was concussed²² and shocked, but the police thought he was the only person injured—until Dr. Travers told his tale.

At half-past nine that night Aunt Rebecca Hoskins was sitting by her fire thinking aggrieved²³ thoughts about the inconsiderateness of nieces who were asked to supper and never turned up, when she was startled by a neighbor, who burst in, exclaiming, "Have you heard about Sandy Pengelly, then, Mrs. Hoskins? Terrible thing, poor little soul, and they don't know if she's likely to live. Police have got the truck driver that hit her—ah, it didn't ought to be allowed, speeding through the place like that at umpty²⁴ miles an hour, they ought to jail him for life—not that that'd be any comfort to poor Bert and Jean."

FIRST READ

Use Reading Skills
Make Predictions What do you think will be the outcome of the accident?

---

22. **concussed.** Having a concussion, or head injury
23. **aggrieved.** Injured, offended
24. **umpty.** Many

in•quire (in kwī´ [ə]r) *v.*, ask

SECOND READ

Analyze Literature
Plot What does this situation suggest about possible resolutions in the plot?

Horrified, Aunt Rebecca put on a coat and went down to her brother's house. She found the family with white shocked faces; Bert and Jean were about to drive off to the hospital where Sandy had been taken, and the twins were crying bitterly. Lob was nowhere to be seen. But Aunt Rebecca was not interested in dogs; she did not <u>inquire</u> about him.

67

"Thank the lord you've come, Beck," said her brother. "Will you stay the night with Don and the twins? Don's out looking for Lob and heaven knows when we'll be back; we may get a bed with Jean's mother in Plymouth."

68

"Oh, if only I'd never invited the poor child," wailed Mrs. Hoskins. But Bert and Jean hardly heard her.

69

That night seemed to last forever. The twins cried themselves to sleep. Don came home very late and grimfaced. Bert and Jean sat in a waiting room of the Western Counties Hospital, but Sandy was unconscious, they were told, and she remained so. All that could be done for her was done. She was given transfusions to replace all the blood she had lost. The broken bones were set and put in slings and cradles.

70

"Is she a healthy girl? Has she a good constitution?"[25] the emergency doctor asked.

71

"Aye, doctor, she is that," Bert said hoarsely. The lump in Jean's throat prevented her from answering; she merely nodded.

72

"Then she ought to have a chance. But I won't conceal from you that her condition is very serious, unless she shows signs of coming out from this coma."[26]

73

But as hour succeeded hour, Sandy showed no signs of recovering consciousness. Her parents sat in the waiting room with haggard[27] faces; sometimes one of them would go to telephone the family at home, or to try to get a little sleep at the home of Granny Pearce, not far away.

74

At noon next day Dr. and Mrs. Travers went to the Pengelly cottage to inquire how Sandy was doing, but the report was gloomy: "Still in a very serious condition." The twins were miserably unhappy. They forgot that they had sometimes called their elder sister bossy and only remembered how often she had shared her pocket money with them,

---

25. **constitution.** Physical makeup or health
26. **coma.** Long and deep state of unconsciousness caused by injury, disease, or poison
27. **haggard.** Appearing extremely tired or worn out
28. **shuttered.** Closed, as if with shutters over a window; in this case, a metaphor for a blank face or a look of being closed down

how she read to them and took them for picnics and helped with their homework. Now there was no Sandy, no Mother and Dad, Don went around with a gray, shuttered[28] face, and worse still, there was no Lob.

75

The Western Counties Hospital is a large one, with dozens of different departments and five or six connected buildings, each with three or four entrances. By that afternoon it became noticeable that a dog seemed to have taken up position outside the hospital, with the fixed intention of getting in. Patiently he would try first one entrance and then another, all the way around, and then begin again. Sometimes he would get a little way inside, following a visitor, but animals were, of course, forbidden, and he was always kindly but firmly turned out again. Sometimes the guard at the main entrance gave him a pat or offered him a bit of sandwich—he looked so wet and beseeching and desperate. But he never ate the sandwich. No one seemed to own him or to know where he came from; Plymouth is a large city and he might have belonged to anybody.

76

At tea time Granny Pearce came through the pouring rain to bring a flask[29] of hot tea with brandy in it to her daughter and son-in-law. Just as she reached the main entrance the guard was gently but forcibly shoving out a large, <u>agitated</u>, soaking-wet Alsatian dog.

77

"No, old fellow, you can *not* come in. Hospitals are for people, not for dogs."

78

"Why, bless me," exclaimed old Mrs. Pearce. "That's Lob! Here, Lob, Lobby boy!"

79

80

Lob ran to her, whining. Mrs. Pearce walked up to the desk.

"I'm sorry, madam, you can't bring that dog in here," the guard said.

81

Mrs. Pearce was a very determined old lady. She looked the porter[30] in the eye.

82

"Now, see here, young man. That dog has walked twenty miles from St. Killan to get to my granddaughter. Heaven knows how he knew she was here, but it's plain he knows. And he ought to have his rights! He ought to get to see her! Do you know," she went on, bristling, "that dog has walked the length of England—*twice*—to be with that girl? And you think you can keep him out with your fiddling rules and regulations?"

---

29. flask. Small container for liquid
30. porter. Doorman

83

Use Reading Skills
Meaning of Words The word face has multiple meanings including the front part of the head or the surface of something. Can you find other words in the selection that have multiple meanings?

ag•i•tat•ed
(aj´ ə tāt' əd) *adj.,* in a nervous or uncomfortable state

FIRST READ ➤

Make Connections
Do you think the grandmother is right to insist on bringing Lob in? Why?

FIRST READ ➤

Use Reading Skills
Clarify How does the description of these men help you understand their roles in the story?

84 "I'll have to ask the medical officer," the guard said weakly.

"You do that, young man." Granny Pearce sat down in a determined manner, shutting her umbrella, and Lob sat patiently dripping at her feet. Every now and then he shook his head, as if to dislodge[31] something heavy that was tied

85 around his neck.

Presently a tired, thin, intelligent-looking man in a white coat came downstairs, with an impressive, silver-haired man in a dark suit, and there was a low-voiced discussion. Granny

86 Pearce eyed them, biding her time.

"Frankly...not much to lose," said the older man. The man

87 in the white coat approached Granny Pearce.

"It's strictly against every rule, but as it's such a serious case we are making an exception," he said to her quietly. "But only

88 outside her bedroom door—and only for a moment or two."

Without a word, Granny Pearce rose and stumped upstairs. Lob followed close to her skirts, as if he knew his

89 hope lay with her.

They waited in the green-floored corridor outside Sandy's room. The door was half-shut. Bert and Jean were inside. Everything was terribly quiet. A nurse came out. The white-coated man asked her something and she shook her head. She had left the door ajar and through it could now be seen a high, narrow bed with a lot of gadgets around it. Sandy lay there, very flat under the covers, very still. Her head was turned away. All Lob's attention was riveted[32] on the bed. He strained

90 toward it, but Granny Pearce clasped his collar firmly.

"I've done a lot for you, my boy, now you behave your-self," she whispered grimly. Lob let out a faint whine, anxious

91 and pleading.

At the sound of that whine, Sandy stirred just a little. She sighed and moved her head the least fraction. Lob whined again. And then Sandy turned her head right over. Her eyes

92 opened, looking at the door.

"Lob?" she murmured—no more than a breath of sound.

93 "Lobby, boy?"

The doctor by Granny Pearce drew a quick, sharp breath. Sandy moved her left arm—the one that was not broken—from below the covers and let her hand dangle down, feeling, as she always did in the mornings, for Lob's furry head. The doctor nodded slowly.

---

31. dislodge. Force something from its secure, firm, or fixed position
32. riveted. Firmly fixed

94   "All right," he whispered. "Let him go to the bedside. But keep a hold of him."

95   Granny Pearce and Lob moved to the bedside. Now she could see Bert and Jean, white-faced and shocked, on the far side of the bed. But she didn't look at them. She looked at the smile on her granddaughter's face as the groping fingers found Lob's wet ears and gently pulled them. "Good boy," whispered Sandy, and fell asleep again.

96   Granny Pearce led Lob out into the passage again. There she let go of him, and he ran off swiftly down the stairs. She would have followed him, but Bert and Jean had come out into the passage, and she spoke to Bert fiercely.

97   "*I* don't know why you were so foolish as not to bring the dog before! Leaving him to find the way here himself—"

98   "But, Mother!" said Jean Pengelly. "That can't have been Lob. What a chance to take! Suppose Sandy hadn't—" She stopped, with her handkerchief pressed to her mouth.

99   "Not Lob? I've known that dog nine years! I suppose I ought to know my own granddaughter's dog?"

100   "Listen, Mother," said Bert. "Lob was killed by the same truck that hit Sandy. Don found him—when he went to look for Sandy's schoolbag. He was—he was dead. Ribs all smashed. No question of that. Don told me on the phone—he and Will Hoskins rowed a half mile out to sea and sank the dog with a lump of concrete tied to his collar. Poor old boy. Still—he was getting on. Couldn't have lasted forever."

101   "*Sank him at sea?* Then what—?"

102   Slowly old Mrs. Pearce, and then the other two, turned to look at the trail of dripping-wet footprints that led down the hospital stairs.

103   In the Pengellys' garden they have a stone, under the palm tree. It says: "Lob. Sandy's dog. Buried at sea." ❧

NOTES

SECOND READ

Analyze Literature
Plot What part of the plot does this scene serve as?

SECOND READ

Use Reading Skills
Draw Conclusions What do you think really happened? What makes you think so?

Mirrors & Windows   Which parts of this story are believable to you? Which parts are less believable? What might be the value in accepting something that cannot be fully explained?

Close Reading Model

Find Meaning	Make Judgments
1. (a) How does Sandy first meet Lob? (b) What is unusual about their next two meetings?	**4.** (a) What qualities does Lob have that are typical of a dog? (b) What is unusual about Lob?
2. (a) How does the Pengelly family come to own Lob? (b) What does the story suggest about those years of ownership?	**5.** What kind of bond exists between Sandy and Lob? Name all the ways in which the girl and her dog seem to be connected.
3. What happens to Sandy and Lob on the night when Sandy is supposed to stay with her Aunt Becky?	**6.** To what extent does this story depend on surprises? Explain your answer using details from the story.

Analyze Literature

Plot Recall that plot is a series of events that relate to a conflict. **Foreshadowing** occurs when an author uses some plot events to hint at events that will happen later in the story. Reread the second half of the story. Which plot events serve as clues to foreshadow the revelation at the story's end?

Foreshadowing Clue	What It Foreshadows
Lob is "soaking-wet."	Lob's dead body was sunk in the sea.

Writing Connection

Informative Writing In a brief literary response, analyze the effect of foreshadowing on the plot. State your main idea in a thesis, or opinion statement. Be sure to give specific examples of foreshadowing and tell how they create tension or suspense, or how they point ahead to things that happen later.

The Goodness of Matt Kaizer page 22

SHORT STORY by Avi

Build Background

Literary Context Similar themes and ideas can be found in most of Avi's novels and short stories. Avi thinks that stories should be entertaining, but he also believes that stories are like maps for the reader to follow into a particular time, place, or experience. He often writes about the complex situations and choices young people face and how they journey through them.

Reader's Context If a good friend dared you to do something you didn't agree with, what would you do? Read to see what happens to a character who can't refuse a dare.

Analyze Literature

Character A **character** takes part in the action of a literary work. Writers create characters (1) by showing what characters say, do, or think, (2) by showing what other characters say or think about them, and (3) by describing the characters' physical appearance. These techniques are called **characterization.** Note what you learn about Matt in this story.

Set Purpose

Voice is the way a writer uses language to reflect his or her unique personality and attitude toward topic, form, and audience. Note examples of the author's conversational voice from the text.

Use Reading Skills

Analyze Cause and Effect Writers often explain why an event takes place. The event is an effect; the why is a cause. Sometimes a single cause has several effects, and an effect can have several causes. As you read this story, use a cause-and-effect chart to keep track of causes and effects.

Cause	Effect
Marley dares Matt to visit Mr. Bataky.	Matt visits Mr. Bataky.

A Short Story by Avi

The Goodness of Matt Kaizer

1 People are always saying, "Nothing's worse than when a kid goes bad." Well, let me tell you, going good isn't all that great either. Tell you what I mean.

2 Back in sixth grade there was a bunch of us who liked nothing better than doing bad stuff. I don't know why. We just liked doing it. And the baddest of the bad was Matt Kaizer.

3 Matt was a tall, thin kid with long, light blond hair that reached his shoulders. He was twelve years old—like I was. His eyes were pale blue and his skin was a vanilla cream that never—no matter the season—seemed to darken, except with dirt. What with the way he looked—so pale and all—plus the fact that he was into wearing extra large blank white T-shirts that reached his knees, we called him "Spirit."

4 Now, there are two important things you need to know about Matt Kaizer. The first was that as far as he was concerned there was nothing good about him at all. Nothing. The second thing was that his father was a minister.[1]

5 Our gang—I'm Marley, and then there was Chuck, Todd, and Nick—loved the fact that Matt was so bad and his father a minister. You know, we were always daring him to do bad things. "Hey, minister's kid!" we'd taunt. "Dare you to..." and we'd challenge him to do something, you know, really gross. Thing is, we could always count on Matt—who wanted to show he wasn't good—to take a dare.

6 For instance: Say there was some dead animal out on the road. We'd all run to Matt and say, "Dare you to pick it up."

7 Matt would look at it—up close and personal—or more than likely poke it with a stick, then pick it up and fling it at one of us.

8 Disgusting stories? Someone would tell one and then say, "Dare you to tell it to Mary Beth Bataky"—the class slug—and Matt would tell it to her—better than anyone else, too.

9 TV and movies? The more blood and gore there was, the more Matt ate it up—if you know what I mean. MTV, cop shows, all that bad stuff, nothing was too gross for him.

FIRST READ →

Use Reading Skills
Visualize Based on this description, visualize what Matt Kaizer looks like.

SECOND READ →

Analyze Literature
Character What are the two important things to know about Matt?

taunt (tOnt) v., challenge or tease in an insulting manner

---

1. **minister.** One who leads the church; clergyperson

10 And it didn't take just dares to get Matt going. No, Matt would do stuff on his own. If anyone blew a toot—even in class—he would bellow, "Who cut the cheese?" He could belch whenever he wanted to, and did, a lot. Spitballs, booger flicking, wedgie yanking, it was all wicked fun for Matt. No way was he going to be good! Not in front of us.

11 Now, his father, the minister, "Rev. Kaizer" we called him, wasn't bad. In fact just the opposite. The guy was easygoing, always dressed decently, and as far as I knew, never raised his voice or acted any way than what he was, a nice man, a good man. Sure, he talked a little funny, like he was reading from a book, but that was all.

12 Did Matt and his father get along? In a way. For example, once I was with Matt after he did something bad—I think he blew his nose on someone's lunch. Rev. Kaizer had learned about it. Instead of getting mad he just gazed at Matt, shook his head, and said, "Matt, I do believe there's goodness in everyone. That goes for you too. Someday you'll find your own goodness. And when you do you'll be free."

13 "I'm not good," Matt insisted.

14 "Well, I think you are," his father said, patiently.

15 Matt grinned. "Long as my friends dare me to do bad things, I'll do 'em."

16 "Never refuse a dare?" his father asked, sadly.

17 "Never," Matt said with pride.

18 Rev. Kaizer sighed, pressed his hands together, and looked toward heaven.

19 So there we were, a bunch of us who knew we were bad and that it was doing bad things that held us together. And the baddest of the bad, like I said, was Matt—the Spirit—Kaizer. But then...oh, man, I'll tell you what happened.

20 One day after school we were hanging out in the playground. The five of us were just sitting around telling disgusting stories, when suddenly Chuck said, "Hey, hear about Mary Beth Bataky?"

21 "What about her?" Matt asked.

22 "Her old man's dying."

23 Right away Matt was interested. "Really?"

24 "It's true, man," Chuck insisted. "He's just about had it."

25 "How come?" I asked.

SECOND READ

Analyze Literature
Character What do Matt and his father disagree about?

26   "Don't know," said Chuck. "He's sick. So sick they sent him home from the hospital. That's why Mary Beth is out. She's waiting for him to die."

27   "Cool," said Matt.

28   Now, Mary Beth was one small straw of a sad slug. She had this bitsy face with pale eyes and two gray lines for lips all framed in a pair of frizzy braids. Her arms were thin and always crossed over her chest, which was usually bundled in a brown sweater. The only bits of color on her were her finger-nails, which, though chewed, were spotted with bright red nail polish—chipped.

29   So when we heard what was going on with Mary Beth and her father, we guys eyed one another, almost knowing what was going to happen next. But, I admit, it was me who said, "Hey, Spirit, I dare you to go and see him."

30   Matt pushed the blond hair out of his face and looked at us with those pale blue, cool-as-ice eyes of his.

31   "Or maybe," Todd said, "you're too chicken, being as you're a minister's kid and all."

32   That did it. Course it did. No way Matt could resist a dare. He got up, casual like. "I'll do it," he said. "Who's coming with me?"

33   To my disgust the other guys backed off. But I accepted. Well, actually, I really didn't think he'd do it.

FIRST READ →

Use Reading Skills
Analyze Cause and Effect Why does Matt feel he has to do what Marley asks?

34   But then, soon as we started off, I began to feel a little nervous. "Matt," I warned. "I think Mary Beth is very religious."

35   "Don't worry. I know about all that stuff."

36   "Yeah, but what would your father say?"

37   "I don't care," he bragged. "Anyway, I'm not going to do anything except look. It'll be neat. Like a horror movie. Maybe I can even touch the guy. A dying body is supposed to be colder than ice."

38   That was Matt. Always taking up the dare and going you one worse.

39   The more he talked the sorrier I was we had dared him to go. Made me really uncomfortable. Which I think he noticed, because he said, "What's the matter, Marley? You scared or something?"

40   "Just seems…"

41   "I know," he taunted, "you're too good!" He belched loudly to make his point that he wasn't. "See you later, dude." He started off.

42   I ran after him. "Do you know where she lives?"

43   "Follow me."

44   "They might not let you see him," I warned.

45   He pulled out some coins. "I'm going to buy some flowers and bring them to him. That's what my mother did when my aunt was sick." He stuffed his mouth full of bubble gum and began blowing and popping.

46   Mary Beth's house was a wooden three-decker with a front porch. Next to the front door were three bell buttons with plastic name labels. The Batakys lived on the first floor.

47   By the time Matt and I got there he had two wilted carnations in his hand. One was dyed blue, the other green. The flower store guy had sold them for ten cents each.

48   "You know," I said in a whisper, as we stood before the door, "her father might already be dead."

49   "Cool," Matt replied, blowing another bubble, while cleaning out an ear with a pinky and inspecting the earwax carefully before smearing it on his shirt. "Did you know your fingernails still grow when you're dead? Same for your hair. I mean, how many really dead people can you get to see?" he said and rang the Batakys' bell.

50   From far off inside there was a buzzing sound.

FIRST READ →

Make Connections
How would you feel at this point if you were Marley?

de·lir·i·ous (di lir> 7 @s) *adj.*, state of being confused; having disordered speech and hallucinations

FIRST READ →

Use Reading Skills
Ask Questions Why does Matt lie to Mary Beth?

51   I was trying to get the nerve to leave when the door opened a crack. Mary Beth—pale eyes rimmed with red—peeked out. There were tears on her cheeks and her lips were crusty. Her small hands—with their spots of red fingernail polish—were trembling.

52   "Oh, hi," she said, her voice small and tense.

53   I felt tight with embarrassment.

54   Matt spoke out loudly. "Hi, Mary Beth. We heard your old man was dying."

55   "Yes, he is," Mary Beth murmured. With one hand on the doorknob it was pretty clear she wanted to retreat² as fast as possible. "He's <u>delirious</u>."

56   "Delirious?" Matt said. "What's that?"

57   "Sort of...crazy."

58   "Oh...wow, sweet!" he said, giving me a nudge of appreciation. Then he held up the blue and green carnations, popped his gum, and said, "I wanted to bring him these."

59   Mary Beth stared at the flowers, but didn't move to take them. All she said was, "My mother's at St. Mary's, praying."

60   Now I really wanted to get out of there. But Matt said, "How about if I gave these to your father?" He held up the flowers again. "Personally."

61   "My mother said he may die any moment," Mary Beth informed us.

62   "I know," Matt said. "So I'd really like to see him before he does."

63   Mary Beth gazed at him. "He's so sick," she said, "he's not up to visiting."

64   "Yeah," Matt pressed, "but, you see, the whole class elected me to come and bring these flowers."

65   His lie worked. "Oh," Mary Beth murmured, and she pulled the door open. "Well, I suppose..."

66   We stepped into a small entrance way. A low-watt bulb dangled over our heads from a wire. Shoes, boots, and broken umbrellas lay in a plastic milk crate.

67   Mary Beth shut the outside door then pushed open an inner one that led to her apartment. It was gloomy and stank of medicine.

68   Matt bopped me on the arm. "Who cut the cheese!" he said with a grin. I looked around at him. He popped another bubble.

---

2. retreat. Draw or lead back; withdraw

69   "Down this way," Mary Beth whispered.

70   We walked down a long hallway. Two pictures were on the walls. They were painted on black velvet. One was a scene of a mountain with snow on it and the sun shining on a stag[3] with antlers. The second picture was of a little girl praying by her bed. Fuzzy gold light streamed in on her from a window.

71   At the end of the hall was a closed door. Mary Beth halted. "He's in here," she whispered. "He's really sick," she warned again. "And he doesn't notice anyone. You really sure you want to see him?"

72   "You bet," Matt said with enthusiasm.

73   "I mean, he won't say hello or anything," Mary Beth said in her low voice. "He just lies there with his eyes open. I don't even know if he sees anything."

74   "Does he have running sores?" Matt asked.

75   I almost gagged.

76   "Running *what?*" Mary Beth asked.

77   "You know, wounds."

78   "It's his liver," Mary Beth explained sadly, while turning the door handle and opening the door. "The doctor said it was all his bad life and drinking."

79   Dark as the hall had been, her father's room was darker. The air was heavy and really stank. A large bed took up most of the space. On one side of the bed was a small chest of drawers. On top of the chest was a lit candle and a glass of water into which a pair of false teeth had been dropped. On the other side of the bed was a wooden chair. Another burning candle was on that.

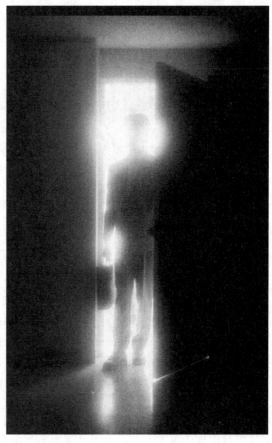

80   On the bed—beneath a brown blanket—lay Mr. Bataky. He was stretched out on his back perfectly straight, like a log. His head and narrow chest were propped up on a pile of four pillows with pictures of flowers on them. At the base of the bed his toes poked up from under the blanket. He was clothed in pajamas dotted with different colored hearts. His hands—looking like a bunch of knuckles—were linked over his chest. His poorly shaven face— yellow in color—was thin. With his cheeks sunken, his nose seemed enormous. His thin hair was uncombed. His breathing was drawn out, almost

---

3. stag. Adult male deer

Analyze Literature
Character What is most striking about Mr. Bataky's appearance?

con·vul·sive (k@n v@l> siv) *adj.*, producing involuntary and uncontrolled muscle movement

whistling, and collapsed into throat gargles[4]—as if he were choking.

81   Worst of all, his eyes were open but he was just staring up, like he was waiting for something to happen in heaven.

82   Mary Beth stepped to one side of the bed. Matt stood at the foot, with me peering over his shoulder. We stared at the dying man. He really looked bad. Awful.

83   "I don't think he'll live long," Mary Beth murmured, her sad voice breaking, her tears dripping.

84   Matt lifted the blue and green carnations. "Mr. Bataky," he shouted, "I brought you some flowers to cheer you up."

85   "His hearing isn't good," Mary Beth said apologetically.

86   Matt looked about for a place to put the flowers, saw the glass with the teeth near Mr. Bataky's head, and moved to put them into the water. In the flickering candlelight, Matt's pale skin, his long blond hair, seemed to glow.

87   Now, just as Matt came up to the head of the bed, Mr. Bataky's eyes shifted. They seemed to fasten on Matt. The old man gave a start, made a <u>convulsive</u> twitch as his eyes positively bulged. Matt, caught in the look, froze.

88   "It's...it's...an *angel*..." Mr. Bataky said in a low, rasping[5] voice. "An angel...from heaven has come to save me."

89   Matt lifted his hand—the one that held the carnations—and tried to place them in the glass of water. Before he could, Mr. Bataky made an unexpected jerk with one of his knobby hands and took hold of Matt's arm. Matt was so surprised he dropped the flowers.

90   "Father!" Mary Beth cried.

91   "Thank...you...for coming, Angel," Mr. Bataky rasped.

92   "No...really," Matt stammered, "I'm not—"

93   "Yes, you're an angel," Mr. Bataky whispered. His eyes—full of tears—were hot with joy.

94   Matt turned red. "No, I'm not..."

95   "Please," Mr. Bataky cried out with amazing energy, "I don't want to die bad." Tears gushed down his hollow cheeks. "You got to help me. Talk to me. Bless[6] me."

96   Matt, speechless for once, gawked at the man.

97   With considerable effort he managed to pry Mr. Bataky's fingers from his arm. Soon as he did he bolted[7] from the room.

Use Reading Skills
Clarify Who does Mr. Bataky think Matt is? What does he think Matt is going to do?

---

4. gargles. Sounds of liquid or air in the throat
5. rasping. Producing a harsh, irritating sound
6. bless. Make holy by religious rite or word; endow with happiness or prosperity
7. bolted. Moved or broke away suddenly or rapidly

98   "Don't abandon me!" Mr. Bataky begged, somehow managing to lift himself up and extend his arms toward the doorway. "Don't!"

99   Frightened, I hurried out after Matt.

100   My buddy was waiting outside, breathing hard. His normally pale face was paler than ever. As we walked away he didn't say anything.

FIRST READ

Use Reading Skills
Analyze Cause and Effect What is the effect of Matt's visit to Mr. Bataky?

101   Now, according to Matt—he told us all this later—what happened was that night Rev. Kaizer called him into his study.

102   "Matt, please sit down."

103   Matt, thinking he was going to get a lecture about visiting Mary Beth's house, sat.

104   His father said, "Matt, I think it's quite wonderful what you've done, going to the home of your classmate's dying father to comfort him."

105   "What do you mean?" Matt asked.

106   Rev. Kaizer smiled sweetly. "A woman by the name of Mrs. Bataky called me. She said her husband was very ill. Dying. She said you—I gather you go to school with her daughter—came to visit him today. Apparently her husband thought you were an…angel. It's the first real sign of life her poor husband has shown in three days. And now, Matt, he's quite desperate to see the angel—you—again."

107   "It's not true," Matt rapped out.

108   "Now, Matt," his father said, "I found the woman's story difficult to believe, too. 'Madam,' I said to her, 'are you quite certain you're talking about *my* son? And are you truly saying your husband really thought he was…an angel?'

109   "And she said, 'Rev. Kaizer—you being a minister I can say it—my husband led a bad, sinful life. But there's something about your son that's making him want to talk about it. Sort of like a confession.[8] Know what I'm saying? I mean, it would do him a lot of good. What I'm asking is, could you get your son to come again? I'm really scared my husband will get worse if he doesn't.'

FIRST READ

Use Reading Skills
Ask Questions What does Mrs. Bataky tell Matt's father?

110   "Matt," said Rev. Kaizer, "I'm proud of you. I think it would be a fine thing if you visited him again."

111   "I'm not an angel," Matt replied in a sulky voice.

112   "I never said *you* were an angel," his father said. "But as I've told you many times, there is goodness inside you as there

---

8. confession. Act of acknowledging one's guilt or wrongdoings

re·pu·ta·tion
(re< py@ t6> sh@n) *n.*, overall character as seen or judged by others

Use Reading Skills
Analyze Cause and Effect How does Rev. Kaizer make Matt go back and visit Mr. Bataky?

Make Connections
How do you think Matt feels about going back to visit Mr. Bataky?

im·plor·ing (im pl0r> i4) *adj.*, crying or calling out intensely; begging

is in everyone. And now you are in the fortunate position of being able to help this sinful man."

113 "I don't want to."

114 "Son, here is a sick man who needs to unburden himself of the unhappy things he's done. I know your <u>reputation</u>. Are you fearful of hearing what Mr. Bataky has to say for himself?"

115 "I don't want to."

116 Rev. Kaizer sat back in his chair, folded his hands over his stomach, smiled gently, and said, "I dare you to go back and listen to Mr. Bataky. I dare you to do goodness."

117 Alarmed, Matt looked up. "But…"

118 "Or are you, being a minister's son, afraid to?"

119 Matt shifted uncomfortably in his seat and tried to avoid his father's steady gaze.

120 Rev. Kaizer offered up a faint smile. "Matt, I thought you never refused a dare."

121 Matt squirmed. Then he said, "I'll go."

122 Anyway, that's the way Matt explained it all. And as he said to me, sadly, "What choice did I have? He dared me."

123 We all saw then that Matt was in a bad place.

124 So the next day when Matt went to visit Mr. Bataky, the bunch of us—me, Chuck, Todd, and Nick—tagged along. We all wanted to see what Matt would do. We figured it *had* to be gross.

125 Mary Beth opened the door. I think she was surprised to see all of us. But she looked at Matt with hope. "Thank you for coming," she said in her tissue paper voice. "He's waiting for you."

126 Matt gave us an <u>imploring</u> look. There was nothing we could do. He disappeared inside. We waited outside.

127 Half an hour later, when he emerged, there was a ton of worry in his eyes. We waited him out, hoping he'd say something ghastly.[9] Didn't say a word.

128 Two blocks from Mary Beth's house I couldn't hold back. "Okay, Matt," I said. "What's happening?"

129 Matt stopped walking. "He really thinks I'm a good angel."

130 "How come?" Nick asked.

131 "I don't know." There was puzzlement in Matt's voice. "He thinks I'm there to give him a second chance at living."

132 "I don't get it," Todd said.

---

9. ghastly. Frightening, terrifying

Close Reading

133   Matt said, "He thinks, you know, if he tells me all his bad stuff, he'll get better."

134   We walked on in silence. Then I said—easy like, "He tell you anything, you know...really bad?"

135   Matt nodded.

136   "Oooo, that's so cool," Nick crowed, figuring Matt would—as he always did—pass it on. "Like what?"

137   Instead of answering, Matt remained silent. Finally, he said, "Not good."

138   "Come on!" we cried. "Tell us!"

139   "He dared me to forgive him. To give him a second chance."

140   "Forgive him for what?" I asked.

141   "All the stuff he's done."

142   "Like what?"

143   "He said he was talking to me...in confidence."

144   "What's that mean?"

145   "Angels can't tell secrets."

146   "You going to believe that?" Todd asked after a bit of silence.

147   Matt stopped walking again. "But...what," he stammered. "What...if it's true?"

148   "What if *what's* true?" I asked.

149   "What if I'm really good inside?"

150   "No way," we all assured him.

151   "But he thinks so," Matt said with real trouble in his voice. "And my father is always saying that too."

152   "Do *you* think so?" Chuck asked.

153   Matt got a flushed[10] look in his eyes. Then he said, "If it is true, it'll be the grossest thing ever."

154   "Hey, maybe it's just a phase," I suggested, hopefully. "You know, something you'll grow out of."

155   Matt gave a shake to his head that suggested he was really seriously confused.

156   Anyway, every afternoon that week, Matt went to see Mr. Bataky. Each time we went with him. For support. We felt we owed him that, though really, we were hoping we'd get to hear some of the bad stuff. But I think we were getting more and more upset, too. See, Matt was changing. Each time he came out of the sick man's room, he looked more and more haggard. And silent.

10. flushed. Red from blushing

SECOND READ

Analyze Literature
Conflict What conflict is Matt experiencing?

Analyze Literature
Character What is the significance of Matt's changing appearance?

157   "What did he say this time?" someone would finally ask.

158   "Really bad," he'd say.

159   "Worse than before?"

160   "Much worse."

161   We'd go on for a bit, not saying anything. Then the pleading would erupt. "Come on! Tell us! What'd he say?"

162   "Can't."

163   "Why?"

164   "I told you: He thinks I'm an angel," Matt said and visibly shuddered. "Angels can't tell secrets."

165   As the week progressed, Matt began to look different from before. He wasn't so grubby. His clothes weren't torn. Things went so fast that by Friday morning, when he came to school, he was actually wearing a tie! Even his hair was cut short and combed. It was awful.

166   "What's the matter with Matt?" we kept asking one another.

167   "I think he's beginning to think he really is an angel," was the only explanation I could give.

168   Finally, on Friday afternoon, when Matt came out of Mary Beth's house, he sat on the front steps, utterly beat. By that time he was dressed all in white: white shirt, pale tie, white pants, and even white sneakers. Not one smudge on him. I'm telling you, it was eerie. Nothing missing but wings.

169   "What's up?" I asked.

170   "The doctor told Mr. Bataky he's better."

171   "You cured him!" cried Nick. "Cool! That mean you don't have to visit him again?"

172   "Right." But Matt just sat there looking as sad as Mary Beth ever did.

173   "What's the matter?" I asked.

174   "I've been sitting and listening to that guy talk and talk about all the things he's done. I mean, I used to think I was bad. But, you know what?"

175   "What?"

176   "I'm not bad. No way. Not compared to him. I even tried to tell him of some of the things I've done."

177   "What did he say?"

178   "He laughed. Said I was only a young angel. Which was the reason I didn't have wings."

Use Reading Skills
Ask Questions How does Matt see himself in comparison to Mr. Bataky?

179   Matt stared down at the ground for a long time. We waited patiently. Finally he looked up. There were tears trickling down his pale face.

180   "I have to face it," he said, turning to look at us, his pals, with real grief in his eyes. "The more I heard that stuff Mr. Bataky did, the more I knew that deep down, inside, I'm just a good kid. I mean, what am I going to do? Don't you see, I'm just like my father said. I'm *good*."

181   You can't believe how miserable he looked. All we could do was sit there and pity him. I mean, just to look at him we knew there weren't going to be any more wicked grins, belches, leers, sly winks, wedgies, or flying boogers.

182   Life went on, but with Matt going angel on us, our gang couldn't hold together. We were finished. Busted.

183   So I'm here to tell you, when a guy turns good, hey, it's rough. ❖

NOTES

SECOND READ

Analyze Literature
Character What does Matt have to face about himself?

Mirrors & Windows

Rev. Kaizer tells Matt, "Someday you'll find your own goodness. And when you do you'll be free." How will Matt be free? Do you agree with Rev. Kaizer that there is goodness in everyone?

_____

_____

_____

_____

Find Meaning	Make Judgments
1. (a) What does the narrator say are the two important things to know about Matt? (b) Why do you think Matt is eager to prove that he is bad?	**4.** (a) What is Mr. Bataky's reaction to the bad things Matt has done? (b) What does Matt's reaction suggest about his personality?
2. (a) What does Matt expect will happen when he goes to see Mr. Bataky? (b) What actually happens? (c) How do you think Matt feels by the end of his first visit?	**5.** (a) What is Matt's central conflict? (b) Is his conflict internal or external? (c) How is his conflict resolved?
3. (a) What does Mr. Bataky tell Matt during his second visit? (b) What effect do Mr. Bataky's words have on Matt?	**6.** Matt's friends seem to think that "it's good to be bad." How does the end of the story suggest that Matt has stopped believing this?

Analyze Literature

Character Authors include many details about a **character** to describe the character's personality and to show what the character learns or how the character changes over time. Based on what you've learned about Matt throughout the story, fill in the chart. Compare the descriptions of Matt at the beginning of the story with those at the end. How has Matt changed?

	Physical Traits	Habits and Behaviors	Thoughts and Feelings
Beginning of Story:	light blond, shoulder-length hair	takes all dares	believes he is bad
End of Story:			

Writing Connection

Informative Writing Write a short **informative essay** analyzing cause and effect in this story. First, state how you think Matt's willingness to take a dare affects the events in the story. Then, explain what happens to Matt as a result of the dare and what he learns from it. Support your points with evidence that maintains meaning or logical order of events.

 page 38

SHORT STORY by Francisco Jiménez

Build Background

Historical Context Migrant farm workers in the United States migrate, or move, from place to place to harvest crops. Starting in 1850, many farm workers began coming to the United States from Mexico. "The Circuit" tells the story of a Mexican-American family who harvests crops in California in the 1950s, following a seasonal route known as a "circuit."

Reader's Context Have you ever moved to a new city or state or had a friend who moved away? How did you feel at the time?

_____

_____

Set Purpose

Preview the Historical Context and the story title. Make a list of five questions you have about the background and the title of the short story with a goal of gaining information and deepening understanding. As you read, notice how the narrator's family's frequent moves and the hard physical labor affect the narrator's emotions and education.

Analyze Literature

Setting The **setting** of a literary work is the time and place in which it happens. In fiction, setting is most often revealed through descriptions of landscape, scenery, buildings, furniture, clothing style, the weather, and the season. It can also be revealed by how characters talk and behave. As you read "The Circuit," notice what details the author uses to create the story's setting.

Use Reading Skills

Analyze Cause and Effect In fiction, actions or plot events often cause future actions or events. The resulting action or event is called an effect. Causes can have multiple effects, and an effect can in turn cause further events. Look for cause-effect relationships in "The Circuit," and track them in a chart like this one.

Cause	Effect
Strawberry season ends.	Panchito and his family must move.

SECOND READ

Analyze Literature
Setting Where are the farm workers? What time of year is it?

FIRST READ

Use Reading Skills
Make Inferences How does the narrator feel about his work?

FIRST READ

Use Reading Skills
Visualize What sensory details does the author include in this scene? What do they mean to the narrator?

A Short Story by Francisco Jiménez

The Circuit

1 It was that time of year again. Ito, the strawberry share-cropper, did not smile. It was natural. The peak of the strawberry season was over and the last few days the workers, most of them *braceros*,[1] were not picking as many boxes as they had during the months of June and July.

2 As the last days of August disappeared, so did the number of *braceros*. Sunday, only one—the best picker—came to work. I liked him. Sometimes we talked during our half-hour lunch break. That is how I found out he was from Jalisco, the same state in Mexico my family was from. That Sunday was the last time I saw him.

3 When the sun had tired and sunk behind the mountains, Ito signaled us that it was time to go home. *"Ya esora,"*[2] he yelled in his broken Spanish. Those were the words I waited for twelve hours a day, every day, seven days a week, week after week. And the thought of not hearing them again saddened me.

4 As we drove home Papá did not say a word. With both hands on the wheel, he stared at the dirt road. My older brother, Roberto, was also silent. He leaned his head back and closed his eyes. Once in a while he cleared from his throat the dust that blew in from outside.

5 Yes, it was that time of year. When I opened the front door to the shack, I stopped. Everything we owned was neatly packed in cardboard boxes. Suddenly I felt even more the weight of hours, days, weeks, and months of work. I sat down on a box. The thought of having to move to Fresno and knowing what was in store for me there brought tears to my eyes.

6 That night I could not sleep. I lay in bed thinking about how much I hated this move.

7 A little before five o'clock in the morning, Papá woke everyone up. A few minutes later, the yelling and screaming of my little brothers and sister, for whom the move was a great adventure, broke the silence of dawn. Shortly, the barking of the dogs accompanied them.

---

1. **braceros** (bra se´ ros) Migrant Mexican farm workers (Spanish)
2. **Ya esora** (ya´ es ô´ rä). The sharecropper is trying to say *Ya es hora,* meaning "It is time" in Spanish.

8 While we packed the breakfast dishes, Papá went outside to start the *"Carachita."*[3] That was the name Papá gave his old black Plymouth. He bought it in a used-car lot in Santa Rosa. Papá was very proud of his little jalopy.[4] He had a right to be proud of it. He spent a lot of time looking at other cars before buying this one. When he finally chose the *Carachita,* he checked it thoroughly before driving it out of the car lot. He examined every inch of the car. He listened to the motor, tilting his head from side to side like a parrot, trying to detect any noises that spelled car trouble. After being satisfied with the looks and sounds of the car, Papá then insisted on knowing who the original owner was. He never did find out from the car salesman, but he bought the car anyway. Papá figured the original owner must have been an important man because behind the rear seat of the car he found a blue necktie.

9 Papá parked the car out in front and left the motor running. *"Listo,"*[5] he yelled. Without saying a word Roberto and I began to carry the boxes out to the car. Roberto carried the two big boxes and I carried the two smaller ones. Papá then threw the mattress on top of the car roof and tied it with ropes to the front and rear bumpers.

10 Everything was packed except Mamá's pot. It was an old large galvanized pot she had picked up at an army <u>surplus</u> store in Santa Maria. The pot had many dents and nicks, and the more dents and nicks it <u>acquired</u> the more Mamá liked it. *"Mi olla,"*[6] she used to say proudly.

sur•plus (sər´ pləs') *n.,* amount that remains after all needs have been met

ac•quire (ə kwī´ [ə]r) *v.,* get as one's own; obtain

11 I held the front door open as Mamá carefully carried out her pot by both handles, making sure not to spill the cooked beans. When she got to the car, Papá reached out to help her with it. Roberto opened the rear car door and Papá gently placed it on the floor behind the front seat. All of us then climbed in. Papá sighed, wiped the sweat from his forehead with his sleeve, and said wearily: *"Es todo."*[7]

---

3. Carachita (kä' rä chē´ tä). Affectionate name for old beat-up-looking car (Spanish)
4. jalopy. Old vehicle in poor condition
5. *Listo* (lēs´ tō). Ready (Spanish)
6. *Mi olla* (mē ō´ yä). My pot (Spanish)
7. *Es todo* (es tō´ dō). That's everything (Spanish)

12   As we drove away, I felt a lump in my throat. I turned around and looked at our little shack for the last time.

13   At sunset we drove into a labor camp near Fresno. Since Papá did not speak English, Mamá asked the camp foreman if he needed any more workers. "We don't need no more," said the foreman, scratching his head. "Check with Sullivan down the road. Can't miss him. He lives in a big white house with a fence around it."

14   When we got there, Mamá walked up to the house. She went through a white gate, past a row of rose bushes, up the stairs to the house. She rang the doorbell. The porch light went on and a tall husky man came out. They exchanged a few words. After the man went in, Mamá clasped her hands and hurried back to the car. "We have work! Mr. Sullivan said we can stay there the whole season," she said, gasping and pointing to an old garage near the stables.

15   The garage was worn out by the years. It had no windows. The walls, eaten by termites, strained to support the roof full of holes. The dirt floor, populated by earthworms, looked like a gray road map.

16   That night, by the light of a kerosene lamp, we unpacked and cleaned our new home. Roberto swept away the loose dirt, leaving the hard ground. Papá plugged the holes in the walls with old newspapers and tin can tops. Mamá fed my little brothers and sister. Papá and Roberto then brought in the mattress and placed it on the far corner of the garage. "Mamá, you and the little ones sleep on the mattress. Roberto, Panchito, and I will sleep outside under the trees," Papá said.

17   Early the next morning Mr. Sullivan showed us where his crop was, and after breakfast, Papá, Roberto, and I headed for the vineyard to pick.

18   Around nine o'clock the temperature had risen to almost one hundred degrees. I was completely soaked in sweat and my mouth felt as if I had been chewing on a handkerchief. I walked over to the end of the row, picked up the jug of water we had brought, and began drinking. "Don't drink too much; you'll get sick," Roberto shouted. No sooner had he said that than I felt sick to my stomach. I dropped to my knees and let the jug roll off my hands. I remained motionless with my eyes glued on the hot sandy ground. All I could hear was the <u>drone</u> of insects. Slowly I began to recover. I poured water over my face and neck and watched the dirty water run down my arms to the ground.

FIRST READ

Use Reading Skills
Visualize From the sensory details given in the text, visualize the garage. What details might make you not want to live there?

SECOND READ

Analyze Literature
Setting Where is Panchito working? What are the conditions like?

drone (drōn) *n.*, constant, low buzzing or humming noise

19   I still felt dizzy when we took a break to eat lunch. It was past two o'clock and we sat underneath a large walnut tree that was on the side of the road. While we ate, Papá jotted down the number of boxes we had picked. Roberto drew designs on the ground with a stick. Suddenly I noticed Papá's face turn pale as he looked down the road. "Here comes the school bus," he whispered loudly in alarm. <u>Instinctively</u>, Roberto and I ran and hid in the vineyards. We did not want to get in trouble for not going to school. The neatly dressed boys about my age got off. They carried books under their arms. After they crossed the street, the bus drove away. Roberto and I came out from hiding and joined Papá. *"Tienen que tener cuidado,"*[8] he warned us.

20   After lunch we went back to work. The sun kept beating down. The buzzing insects, the wet sweat, and the hot dry dust made the afternoon seem to last forever. Finally the mountains around the valley reached out and swallowed the sun. Within an hour it was too dark to continue picking. The vines blanketed the grapes, making it difficult to see the bunches. *"Vámonos,"*[9] said Papá, signaling to us that it was time to quit work. Papá then took out a pencil and began to figure out how much we had earned our first day. He wrote down numbers, crossed some out, wrote down some more. *"Quince,"*[10] he murmured.

21   When we arrived home, we took a cold shower underneath a water hose. We then sat down to eat dinner around some wooden crates that served as a table. Mamá had cooked a special meal for us. We had rice and tortillas with *"carne con chile,"*[11] my favorite dish.

22   The next morning I could hardly move. My body ached all over. I felt little control over my arms and legs. This feeling went on every morning for days until my muscles finally got used to the work.

23   It was Monday, the first week of November. The grape season was over and I could now go to school. I woke up early that morning and lay in bed, looking at the stars and <u>savoring</u> the thought of not going to work and of starting sixth grade for the first time that year. Since I could not sleep, I decided to get up and join Papá and Roberto at breakfast. I sat at the

in • stinc • tive • ly
(in stiŋ[k]´ tiv lē) *adv.*, with a natural urge toward a particular behavior

FIRST READ

Make Connections
How do the descriptions of farm labor in the vineyard affect your feelings about Panchito?

sa • vor (sā´ vər) v., enjoy

---

8. *Tienen que tener cuidado.* You have to be careful. (Spanish)
9. *Vámonos* (vä´ mô nōs'). Let's go. (Spanish)
10. *Quince* (kēn´ sā). Fifteen (Spanish)
11. *carne con chile* (kär´ nā kôn chē´ lā). Meat cooked with hot peppers (Spanish)

table across from Roberto, but I kept my head down. I did not want to look up and face him. I knew he was sad. He was not going to school today. He was not going tomorrow, or next week, or next month. He would not go until the cotton season was over, and that was sometime in February. I rubbed my hands together and watched the dry, acid stained skin fall to the floor in little rolls.

24   When Papá and Roberto left for work, I felt relief. I walked to the top of a small grade next to the shack and watched the *Carachita* disappear in the distance in a cloud of dust.

25   Two hours later, around eight o'clock, I stood by the side of the road waiting for school bus number twenty. When it arrived I climbed in. Everyone was busy either talking or yelling. I sat in an empty seat in the back.

26   When the bus stopped in front of the school, I felt very nervous. I looked out the bus window and saw boys and girls carrying books under their arms. I put my hands in my pant pockets and walked to the principal's office. When I entered I heard a woman's voice say: "May I help you?" I was startled. I had not heard English for months. For a few seconds I remained speechless. I looked at the lady who waited for an answer. My first instinct was to answer her in Spanish, but I held back. Finally, after struggling for English words, I managed to tell her that I wanted to enroll in the sixth grade. After answering many questions, I was led to the classroom.

27   Mr. Lema, the sixth grade teacher, greeted me and assigned me a desk. He then introduced me to the class. I was so nervous and scared at that moment when everyone's eyes were on me that I wished I were with Papá and Roberto picking cotton. After taking roll, Mr. Lema gave the class the assignment for the first hour. "The first thing we have to do this morning is finish reading the story we began yesterday," he said enthusiastically. He walked up to me, handed me an English book, and asked me to read. "We are on page 125," he said politely. When I heard this, I felt my blood rush to my head; I felt dizzy. "Would you like to read?" he asked hesitantly. I opened the book to page 125. My mouth was dry. My eyes began to water. I could not begin. "You can read later," Mr. Lema said understandingly.

28   During recess I went into the rest room and opened my English book to page 125. I began to read in a low voice,

FIRST READ

Make Connections
How do Panchito's experiences in school affect your feelings about him?

pretending I was in class. There were many words I did not know. I closed the book and headed back to the classroom.

29   Mr. Lema was sitting at his desk correcting papers. When I entered he looked up at me and smiled. I felt better. I walked up to him and asked if he could help me with the new words. "Gladly," he said.

30   The rest of the month I spent my lunch hours working on English with Mr. Lema, my best friend at school.

31   One Friday during lunch hour Mr. Lema asked me to take a walk with him to the music room. "Do you like music?" he asked me as we entered the building. "Yes, I like *corridos*,"[12] I answered. He then picked up a trumpet, blew on it, and handed it to me. The sound gave me goose bumps. I knew that sound. I had heard it in many *corridos*. "How would you like to learn how to play it?" he asked. He must have read my face because before I could answer, he added: "I'll teach you how to play it during our lunch hours."

32   That day I could hardly wait to tell Papá and Mamá the great news. As I got off the bus, my little brothers and sister ran up to meet me. They were yelling and screaming. I thought they were happy to see me, but when I opened the door to our shack, I saw that everything we owned was neatly packed in cardboard boxes. ✤

---

12. **corridos** (kôr ē´ dōs). Songs that are slow and romantic (Spanish)

FIRST READ

Use Reading Skills
Make Inferences How does Panchito feel when Mr. Lema offers to give him trumpet lessons?

Mirrors & Windows   How does this story help you understand the challenges of life as a migrant farm worker? How does it help you understand the difficulties faced by students in the United States who don't speak much English?

_____

_____

_____

_____

Find Meaning	Make Judgments
1. (a) In the first part of the story, where does the family move? (b) Why does Panchito say, "Knowing what was in store for me there brought tears to my eyes"?	**4.** (a) What work does the family do? (b) How is Panchito's life different from the life of an average student in your school?
2. (a) What is Panchito's attitude toward school? (b) What challenges does he face when he goes to school?	**5.** (a) Why do Panchito and Roberto hide when they see the school bus? (b) What does this suggest about their status as farm workers?
3. (a) How does Mr. Lema help Panchito with some of his challenges in school? (b) How do you think his help affects Panchit?	**6.** (a) At the end of the story, what details does the author use to show that the family is moving? (b) How do you think Panchito feels when he realizes his family is moving again?

Analyze Literature

Setting Sensory details are words and phrases that describe how things look, sound, smell, taste, or feel. Authors use **sensory details** to help create the **setting** of a story. In a chart, list the sensory details the author uses to describe the vineyard where Panchito works. How would you describe the setting in your own words? Why might it be difficult to do harvesting work in this setting?

Sight	Sound	Touch	Taste	Smell
sun sinking behind mountains				

Writing Connection

Argumentative Writing Write an **editorial** for a newspaper arguing for special school programs for children of migrant workers, based around the farming seasons. In the first paragraph, include a brief statement of why such programs are needed, and include information about a migrant child's work schedule. In the second paragraph, describe Panchito's attitude toward education as an example of why migrant children would want special programs. Share your editorial with the class.

Unit 2

Tuesday of the Other June page 96

SHORT STORY by Norma Fox Mazer

Build Background

Literary Context In this story, June's mother tells June to "turn the other cheek." This commonly used expression suggests accepting aggression or injury without returning it. How to respond to aggression or injustice is a recurring, or repeating, theme in literature across time and cultures.

Reader's Context When has someone picked on or bullied you? How did you handle the situation? What do you think is the best way to solve the problem of bullying?

_____

_____

Set Purpose

Voice is the way a writer uses language to reflect his or her unique personality and attitude toward topic, form, and audience. Note examples of the author's conversational voice from the text.

Use Reading Skills

Draw Conclusions To draw conclusions, gather key ideas from the story and examine the details that support them. Then decide what they mean. Make a log to record key ideas and conclusions.

Analyze Literature

Point of View The vantage point from which a story is told is the **point of view.** If the story is told from the first-person point of view, the narrator (the person or character telling the story) uses _I_, _my_, _me_, and _mine_. The narrator might also use _we_, _us_, and _our_. Most importantly, the narrator reveals what only he or she could know, such as personal or secret feelings. As you read the story, notice how the first-person point of view helps you understand the inner thoughts of the narrator.

> **Key Ideas:** June is an only child. She lives with her mother.

> **Supporting Details:** "It's just you and me, two women alone in the world, June darling of my heart."

> **Overall Conclusions:** June and her mother are close.

SECOND READ ▶

Analyze Literature
Point of View Who is telling the story?

SECOND READ ▶

Analyze Literature
Point of View What have you learned so far about the relationship between June and her mom?

FIRST READ ▶

Make Connections
What fears, feelings, or actions do you share with June?

A Short Story by Norma Fox Mazer

Tuesday of the Other June

1 Be good, be good, be good, be good, my Junie," my mother sang as she combed my hair; a song, a story, a croon,[1] a plea. "It's just you and me, two women alone in the world, June darling of my heart, we have enough troubles getting by, we surely don't need a single one more, so you keep your sweet self out of fighting and all that bad stuff. People can be little-hearted, but turn the other cheek,[2] smile at the world, and the world'll surely smile back."

2 We stood in front of the mirror as she combed my hair, combed and brushed and smoothed. Her head came just above mine, she said when I grew another inch she'd stand on a stool to brush my hair. "I'm not giving up this pleasure!" And she laughed her long honey laugh.

3 My mother was April, my grandmother had been May, I was June. "And someday," said my mother, "you'll have a daughter of your own. What will you name her?"

4 "January!" I'd yell when I was little. "February! No, November!" My mother laughed her honey laugh. She had little emerald eyes that warmed me like the sun.

5 Every day when I went to school, she went to work. "Sometimes I stop what I'm doing," she said, "lay down my tools, and stop everything, because all I can think about is you. Wondering what you're doing and if you need me. Now, Junie, if anyone ever bothers you—"

6 "—I walk away, run away, come on home as fast as my feet will take me," I recited.

7 "Yes. You come to me. You just bring me your trouble, because I'm here on this earth to love you and take care of you."

8 I was safe with her. Still, sometimes I woke up at night and heard footsteps slowly creeping up the stairs. It wasn't my mother, she was asleep in the bed across the room, so it was robbers, thieves, and murderers, creeping slowly...slowly... slowly toward my bed.

9 I stuffed my hand into my mouth. If I screamed and woke her, she'd be tired at work tomorrow. The robbers and thieves filled the warm darkness and slipped across the floor

---

1. **croon.** Act of singing softly or gently
2. **turn the other cheek.** Do not fight back; calmly accept when someone is mean or harmful

more quietly than cats. Rigid under the covers, I stared at the shifting dark and bit my knuckles and never knew when I fell asleep again.

10   In the morning we sang in the kitchen. "Bill Grogan's goat! Was feelin' fine! Ate three red shirts, right off the line!" I made sandwiches for our lunches, she made pancakes for breakfast, but all she ate was one pancake and a cup of coffee. "Gotta fly, can't be late."

11   I wanted to be rich and take care of her. She worked too hard, her pretty hair had gray in it that she joked about. "Someday," I said, "I'll buy you a real house and you'll never work in a pot factory again."

12   "Such delicious plans," she said. She checked the windows to see if they were locked. "Do you have your key?"

13   I lifted it from the chain around my neck.

14   "And you'll come right home from school and—"

15   "—I won't light fires or let strangers into the house and I won't tell anyone on the phone that I'm here alone," I finished for her.

16   "I know, I'm just your old worrywart[3] mother." She kissed me twice, once on each cheek. "But you are my June, my only June, the only June."

17   She was wrong, there was another June. I met her when we stood next to each other at the edge of the pool the first day of swimming class in the Community Center.

18   "What's your name?" She had a deep growly voice.

19   "June. What's yours?"

20   She stared at me. "June."

21   "We have the same name."

22   "No we don't. June is my name, and I don't give you permission to use it. Your name is Fish Eyes." She pinched me hard. "Got it, Fish Eyes?"

23   The next Tuesday, the Other June again stood next to me at the edge of the pool. "What's your name?"

24   "June."

25   "Wrong. Your—name—is—Fish—Eyes."

26   "June."

27   "Fish Eyes, you are really stupid." She shoved me into the pool.

28   The swimming teacher looked up, frowning, from her chart. "No one in the water yet."

FIRST READ

Use Reading Skills
Draw Conclusions What do the Other June's words and actions reveal about her?

---

3. worrywart. Person who worries a great deal

29   Later, in the locker room, I dressed quickly and wrapped my wet suit in the towel. The Other June pulled on her jeans. "You guys see that bathing suit Fish Eyes was wearing? Her mother found it in a trash can."

30   "She did not!"

31   The Other June grabbed my fingers and twisted. "Where'd she find your bathing suit?"

32   "She bought it, let me go."

33   "Poor little stupid Fish Eyes is crying. Oh, boo hoo hoo, poor little Fish Eyes."

34   After that, everyone called me Fish Eyes. And every Tuesday, wherever I was, there was also the Other June—at the edge of the pool, in the pool, in the locker room. In the water, she swam alongside me, blowing and huffing, knocking into me. In the locker room, she stepped on my feet, pinched my arms, hid my blouse, and knotted my braids together. She had large square teeth, she was shorter than I was, but heavier, with bigger bones and square hands. If I met her outside on the street, carrying her bathing suit and towel, she'd walk toward me, smiling a square, friendly smile. "Oh well, if it isn't Fish Eyes." Then she'd punch me, *blam*! her whole solid weight hitting me.

35   I didn't know what to do about her. She was training me like a dog. After a few weeks of this, she only had to look at me, only had to growl, "I'm going to get you, Fish Eyes," for my heart to slink like a whipped dog down into my stomach.

FIRST READ

Make Connections
How would you react if you were in June's position?

Close Reading   © Carnegie Learning, Inc.

My arms were covered with bruises. When my mother noticed, I made up a story about tripping on the sidewalk.

36   My weeks were no longer Tuesday, Wednesday, Thursday, and so on. Tuesday was Awfulday. Wednesday was Badday. (The Tuesday bad feelings were still there.) Thursday was Betterday and Friday was Safeday. Saturday was Goodday, but Sunday was Toosoonday, and Monday—Monday was nothing but the day before Awfulday.

37   I tried to slow down time. Especially on the weekends, I stayed close by my mother, doing everything with her, shopping, cooking, cleaning, going to the laundromat. "Aw, sweetie, go play with your friends."

38   "No, I'd rather be with you." I wouldn't look at the clock or listen to the radio (they were always telling you the date and the time). I did special magic things to keep the day from going away, rapping my knuckles six times on the bathroom door six times a day and never, ever touching the chipped place on my bureau. But always I woke up to the day before Tuesday, and always, no matter how many times I circled the worn spot in the living-room rug or counted twenty-five cracks in the ceiling, Monday disappeared and once again it was Tuesday.

39   The Other June got bored with calling me Fish Eyes. Buffalo Brain came next, but as soon as everyone knew that, she renamed me Turkey Nose.

40   Now at night it wasn't robbers creeping up the stairs, but the Other June, coming to <u>torment</u> me. When I finally fell asleep, I dreamed of kicking her, punching, biting, pinching. In the morning I remembered my dreams and felt brave and strong. And then I remembered all the things my mother had taught me and told me.

41   *Be good, be good, be good, it's just us two women alone in the world*...Oh, but if it weren't, if my father wasn't long gone, if we'd had someone else to fall back on, if my mother's mother and daddy weren't dead all these years, if my father's daddy wanted to know us instead of being glad to forget us— oh, then I would have punched the Other June with a frisky heart, I would have grabbed her arm at poolside and bitten her like the dog she had made of me.

42   One night, when my mother came home from work, she said, "Junie, listen to this. We're moving!"

© Carnegie Learning, Inc.

Close Reading

NOTES

SECOND READ

Analyze Literature
Point of View What do you learn about June that no other character could tell you?

tor•ment (tôr ment´) *v.*, cause another to feel extreme mental or physical pain

FIRST READ

Use Reading Skills
Make Predictions What do you think the narrator will do the next time the Other June is mean to her?

FIRST READ →

Use Reading Skills
Draw Conclusions Why does June want to move right away?

stag·ger (sta´ gər) v., move unsteadily, as if about to fall over

43   Alaska, I thought. Florida. Arizona. Someplace far away and wonderful, someplace without the Other June.

44   "Wait till you hear this deal. We are going to be caretakers, troubleshooters[4] for an eight-family apartment building. Fifty-six Blue Hill Street. Not janitors, we don't do any of the heavy work. April and June, Troubleshooters, Incorporated. If a tenant has a complaint or a problem, she comes to us and we either take care of it or call the janitor for service. And for that little bit of work, we get to live rent free!" She swept me around in a dance. "Okay? You like it? I do!"

45   So. Not anywhere else, really. All the same, maybe too far to go to swimming class? "Can we move right away? Today?"

46   "Gimme a break, sweetie. We've got to pack, do a thousand things. I've got to line up someone with a truck to help us. Six weeks, Saturday the fifteenth." She circled it on the calendar. It was the Saturday after the last day of swimming class.

47   Soon, we had boxes lying everywhere, filled with clothes and towels and glasses wrapped in newspaper. Bit by bit, we cleared the rooms, leaving only what we needed right now. The dining-room table <u>staggered</u> on a bunched-up rug, our bureaus inched toward the front door like patient cows. On the calendar in the kitchen, my mother marked off the days until we moved, but the only days I thought about were Tuesdays—Awfuldays. Nothing else was real except the too fast passing of time, moving toward each Tuesday...away from Tuesday...toward Tuesday....

48   And it seemed to me that this would go on forever, that Tuesdays would come forever and I would be forever trapped by the side of the pool, the Other June whispering *Buffalo Brain Fish Eyes Turkey Nose* into my ear, while she ground her elbow into my side and smiled her square smile at the swimming teacher.

49   And then it ended. It was the last day of swimming class. The last Tuesday. We had all passed our tests and, as if in celebration, the Other June only pinched me twice. "And now," our swimming teacher said, "all of you are ready for the Advanced Class, which starts in just one month. I have a sign-up slip here. Please put your name down before you leave." Everyone but me crowded around. I went to the locker

---

4. troubleshooters. People who solve problems before they become serious

room and pulled on my clothes as fast as possible. The Other June burst through the door just as I was leaving. "Goodbye," I yelled, "good riddance to bad trash!"[5] Before she could pinch me again, I ran past her and then ran all the way home, singing, "Goodbye...goodbye...goodbye, good riddance to bad trash!"

NOTES

FIRST READ

Use Reading Skills
Draw Conclusions How does June feel right now? How do you know?

50   Later, my mother carefully untied the blue ribbon around my swimming class diploma. "Look at this! Well, isn't this wonderful! You are on your way, you might turn into an Olympic swimmer, you never know what life will bring."

51   "I don't want to take more lessons."

52   "Oh, sweetie, it's great to be a good swimmer." But then, looking into my face, she said, "No, no, no, don't worry, you don't have to."

53   The next morning, I woke up hungry for the first time in weeks. No more swimming class. No more Baddays and Awfuldays. No more Tuesdays of the Other June. In the kitchen, I made hot cocoa to go with my mother's corn muffins. "It's Wednesday, Mom," I said, stirring the cocoa. "My favorite day."

54   "Since when?"

55   "Since this morning." I turned on the radio so I could hear the announcer tell the time, the temperature, and the day.

SECOND READ

Analyze Literature
Point of View How does knowing June's inner thoughts and feelings help you understand her words and actions?

56   Thursday for breakfast I made cinnamon toast, Friday my mother made pancakes, and on Saturday, before we moved, we ate the last slices of bread and cleaned out the peanut butter jar.

57   "Some breakfast," Tilly said. "Hello, you must be June." She shook my hand. She was a friend of my mother's from work, she wore big hoop earrings, sandals, and a skirt as dazzling as a rainbow. She came in a truck with John to help us move our things.

58   John shouted cheerfully at me, "So you're moving." An enormous man with a face covered with little brown bumps. Was he afraid his voice wouldn't travel the distance from his mouth to my ear? "You looking at my moles?" he shouted, and he heaved our big green flowered chair down the stairs. "Don't worry, they don't bite. Ha, ha, ha!" Behind him came my mother and Tilly balancing a bureau between them, and behind them I carried a lamp and the round, flowered

---

5. good riddance to bad trash. Expression of relief that someone or something troublesome is gone

Mexican tray that was my mother's favorite. She had found it at a garage sale and said it was as close to foreign travel as we would ever get.

59   The night before, we had loaded our car, stuffing in bags and boxes until there was barely room for the two of us. But it was only when we were in the car, when we drove past Abdo's Grocery, where they always gave us credit, when I turned for a last look at our street—it was only then that I understood we were truly going to live somewhere else, in another apartment, in another place mysteriously called Blue Hill Street.

60   Tilly's truck followed our car.

61   "Oh, I'm so excited," my mother said. She laughed. "You'd think we were going across the country."

62   Our old car wheezed up a long steep hill. Blue Hill Street. I looked from one side to the other, trying to see everything.

63   My mother drove over the <u>crest</u> of the hill. "And now—ta da!—our new home."

crest (krest) *n.*, peak of a mountain or hill

64   "Which house? Which one?" I looked out the window and what I saw was the Other June. She was sprawled on the stoop of a pink house, lounging back on her elbows, legs outspread, her jaws working on a wad of gum. I slid down into the seat, but it was too late. I was sure she had seen me.

65   My mother turned into a driveway next to a big white building with a tiny porch. She leaned on the steering wheel. "See that window there, that's our living-room window...and that one over there, that's your bedroom...."

66   We went into the house, down a dim cool hall. In our new apartment, the wooden floors clicked under our shoes, and my mother showed me everything. Her voice echoed in the empty rooms. I followed her around in a <u>daze</u>. Had I imagined seeing the Other June? Maybe I'd seen another girl who looked like her. A double. That could happen.

daze (dāz) *n.*, state of surprised or stunned confusion

67   "Ho yo, where do you want this chair?" John appeared in the doorway. We brought in boxes and bags and beds and stopped only to eat pizza and drink orange juice from the carton.

68   "June's so quiet, do you think she'll adjust all right?" I heard Tilly say to my mother.

69   "Oh, definitely. She'll make a wonderful adjustment. She's just getting used to things."

70   But I thought that if the Other June lived on the same street as I did, I would never get used to things.

71   That night I slept in my own bed, with my own pillow and blanket, but with floors that creaked in strange voices and walls with cracks I didn't recognize. I didn't feel either happy or unhappy. It was as if I were waiting for something.

72   Monday, when the principal of Blue Hill Street School left me in Mr. Morrisey's classroom, I knew what I'd been waiting for. In that room full of strange kids, there was one person I knew. She smiled her square smile, raised her hand, and said, "She can sit next to me, Mr. Morrisey."

73   "Very nice of you, June M. Okay, June T, take your seat. I'll try not to get you two Junes mixed up."

74   I sat down next to her. She pinched my arm. "Good riddance to bad trash," she <u>mocked</u>.

75   I was back in the Tuesday swimming class only now it was worse, because every day would be Awfulday. The pinching had already started. Soon, I knew, on the playground and in the halls, kids would pass me, grinning. "Hiya, Fish Eyes."

76   The Other June followed me around during recess that day, droning[6] in my ear, "You are my slave, you must do

---

6. **droning.** Humming or buzzing for a long time

NOTES

FIRST READ

Use Reading Skills
Ask Questions Why does the Other June say this? What effect do you think it has on June?

mock (mäk) *v.*, imitate scornfully

everything I say, I am your master, say it, say, 'Yes, master, you are my master.' "

77   I pressed my lips together, clapped my hands over my ears, but without hope. Wasn't it only a matter of time before I said the hateful words?

78   "How was school?" my mother said that night.

79   "Okay."

80   She put a pile of towels in a bureau drawer. "Try not to be sad about missing your old friends, sweetie, there'll be new ones."

81   The next morning, the Other June was waiting for me when I left the house. "Did your mother get you that blouse in the garbage dump?" She butted me, shoving me against a tree. "Don't you speak anymore, Fish Eyes?" Grabbing my chin in her hands, she pried open my mouth. "Oh, ha ha, I thought you lost your tongue."

82   We went on to school. I sank down into my seat, my head on my arms. "June T, are you all right?" Mr. Morrisey asked. I nodded. My head was almost too heavy to lift.

83   The Other June went to the pencil sharpener. Round and round she whirled the handle. Walking back, looking at me, she held the three sharp pencils like three little knives.

84   Someone knocked on the door. Mr. Morrisey went out into the hall. Paper planes burst into the air, flying from desk to desk. Someone turned on a transistor radio. And the Other June, coming closer, smiled and licked her lips like a cat sleepily preparing to gulp down a mouse.

85   I remembered my dream of kicking her, punching, biting her like a dog.

86   Then my mother spoke quickly in my ear: *Turn the other cheek, my Junie, smile at the world and the world'll surely smile back.*

87   But I had turned the other cheek and it was slapped. I had smiled and the world hadn't smiled back. I couldn't run home as fast as my feet would take me, I had to stay in school—and in school there was the Other June. Every morning, there would be the Other June, and every afternoon, and every day, all day, there would be the Other June.

88   She frisked down the aisle, stabbing the pencils in the air toward me. A boy stood up on his desk and bowed. "My fans," he said, "I greet you." My arm twitched and throbbed, as if the Other June's pencils had already poked through the skin. She came closer, smiling her Tuesday smile.

FIRST READ

Make Connections
How familiar is this scene to you? Why?

FIRST READ

Use Reading Skills
Make Inferences What conclusion do you think June is reaching?

Close Reading

89   "No," I whispered, *"no."* The word took wings and flew me to my feet, in front of the Other June. *"Noooooo."* It flew out of my mouth into her surprised face.

90   The boy on the desk turned toward us. "You said something, my devoted fans?"

91   "No," I said to the Other June. "Oh, no! No. No. No. No more." I pushed away the hand that held the pencils.

92   The Other June's eyes opened, popped wide like the eyes of somebody in a cartoon. It made me laugh. The boy on the desk laughed, and then the other kids were laughing, too.

93   "No," I said again, because it felt so good to say it. "No, no, no, no." I leaned toward the Other June, put my finger against her chest. Her cheeks turned red, she squawked something— it sounded like "Eeeraaghyou!"—and she stepped back. She stepped away from me.

94   The door banged, the airplanes disappeared, and Mr. Morrisey walked to his desk. "Okay. Okay. Let's get back to work. Kevin Clark, how about it?" Kevin jumped off the desk and Mr. Morrisey picked up a piece of chalk. "All right, class—" He stopped and looked at me and the Other June. "You two Junes, what's going on there?"

95   I tried it again. My finger against her chest. Then the words. "No—more." And she stepped back another step. I sat down at my desk.

96   "June M.," Mr. Morrisey said.

97   She turned around, staring at him with that big-eyed cartoon look. After a moment she sat down at her desk with a loud slapping sound.

98   Even Mr. Morrisey laughed.

99   And sitting at my desk, twirling my braids, I knew this was the last Tuesday of the Other June. ❖

Use Reading Skills
Meaning of Words The word *feet* has multiple meanings. Can you find other words in the selection that have multiple meanings?

Mirrors & Windows

June ultimately rejects her mother's advice to "turn the other cheek" and stands up for herself. How would you have reacted in her situation? When might it be important to make your own decisions, despite others' advice?

_____

_____

_____

_____

Close Reading Model

Find Meaning	Make Judgments
1. (a) What advice does June's mother give her about dealing with mean people? (b) Give an example of a time in the story when June takes her mother's advice.	**4.** (a) How does the narrator change in this story? (b) What causes her to change?
2. (a) Who is the Other June? (b) Why is she mean to the narrator?	**5.** Does the Other June also change? Explain your answer.
3. Why can't the narrator get away from the Other June?	**6.** (a) Why is the story called "Tuesday of the Other June"? (b) Do you think this is a good title? Explain your answer.

Analyze Literature

Point of View June is a quiet girl who doesn't say much in the story. Yet, because the story uses first-person point of view, you find out a great deal about what she thinks and feels. Use a chart to list scenes in which you learn June's inner thoughts and feelings. Tell what you learn about June from each scene you list.

Scene from the Story	What I Learn About June's Inner Thoughts and Feelings
June's mother combs her hair and sings to her.	June and her mother are close.

Writing Connection

Informative Writing Review the draw conclusions log you created as you read the story and your point of view chart. Then write a **literary response.** In your response, tell how point of view affects the characterization of June in the story. State your main idea in a thesis. To support your points, cite specific examples of what June says, does, thinks, or feels. Share your response with the class.

The Bracelet page 110

SHORT STORY by Yoshiko Uchida

Build Background

Historical Context When Japan bombed Pearl Harbor in 1941, the United States declared war on Japan. By March 1942, all people of Japanese descent—even U.S. citizens—were forbidden to live freely in this country. During what has become known as the Japanese internment, the government moved roughly 110,000 people to relocation centers with poor living conditions. The family in this story is just one of the thousands that had to leave behind everything they had.

Reader's Context Have you ever had to move or leave a place behind? What do people go through when they must leave the people and places they call home?

Analyze Literature

Theme A **theme** is a central idea in a literary work. The theme is not the topic but is usually a statement about the topic. Often a theme is a general or universal statement about life. The theme is usually implied, meaning the reader has to figure it out. As you read the story, ask yourself what theme it suggests.

Set Purpose

As you read, look for the theme, or the main idea, of the story. Remember than an author's purpose is the reason for writing and the theme is the message the author is trying to get across. Explaining the author's purpose will help you understand the important lesson included in the theme.

Use Reading Skills

Evaluate Author's Purpose Why did Uchida write this story? Once you decide, evaluate her purpose by determining how well Uchida achieved her goal. For example, if her purpose is to entertain, identify details in the story that did or did not hold your interest. Make a chart to record your evaluation.

Author's Purpose:

Details:	My Evaluation:

A Short Story by Yoshiko Uchida

The Bracelet

1 "Mama, is it time to go?" I hadn't planned to cry, but the tears came suddenly, and I wiped them away with the back of my hand. I didn't want my older sister to see me crying.

2 "It's almost time, Ruri," my mother said gently. Her face was filled with a kind of sadness I had never seen before.

3 I looked around at my empty room. The clothes that Mama always told me to hang up in the closet, the junk piled on my dresser, the old rag doll I could never bear to part with—they were all gone. There was nothing left in my room, and there was nothing left in the rest of the house. The rugs and furniture were gone, the pictures and drapes were down, and the closets and cupboards were empty. The house was like a gift box after the nice thing inside was gone; just a lot of nothingness.

4 It was almost time to leave our home, but we weren't moving to a nicer house or to a new town. It was April 21, 1942. The United States and Japan were at war, and every Japanese person on the West Coast was being evacuated[1] by the government to a concentration camp. Mama, my sister Keiko, and I were being sent from our home, and out of Berkeley,[2] and eventually out of California.

5 The doorbell rang, and I ran to answer it before my sister could. I thought maybe by some miracle a messenger from the government might be standing there, tall and proper and buttoned into a uniform, come to tell us it was all a terrible mistake, that we wouldn't have to leave after all. Or maybe the messenger would have a telegram from Papa, who was <u>interned</u> in a prisoner-of-war camp in Montana because he had worked for a Japanese business firm.

6 The FBI[3] had come to pick up Papa and hundreds of other Japanese community leaders on the very day that Japanese planes had bombed Pearl Harbor. The government thought they were dangerous enemy <u>aliens</u>. If it weren't so sad, it would have been funny. Papa could no more be dangerous than the mayor of our city, and he was every bit as loyal to the United States. He had lived here since 1917.

1. **evacuated.** Removed, usually in haste or because of a threat
2. **Berkeley.** City in California near the Pacific coast
3. **FBI.** Federal Bureau of Investigation, a national law enforcement agency

---

FIRST READ ➡

Use Reading Skills
Evaluate Author's Purpose What do these details suggest about the author's purpose?

in·tern (in´ tərn') *v.*, send away and confine

SECOND READ ➡

Analyze Literature
Theme What message about the Japanese internment do these details suggest?

a·li·en (ā´ lē ən) *n.*, person who does not belong; foreigner

7   When I opened the door, it wasn't a messenger from anywhere. It was my best friend, Laurie Madison, from next door. She was holding a package wrapped up like a birthday present, but she wasn't wearing her party dress, and her face drooped like a <u>wilted</u> tulip.

8   "Hi," she said. "I came to say goodbye."

9   She thrust the present at me and told me it was something to take to camp. "It's a bracelet," she said before I could open the package. "Put it on so you won't have to pack it." She knew I didn't have one inch of space left in my suitcase. We had been instructed to take only what we could carry into camp, and Mama had told us that we could each take only two suitcases.

10   "Then how are we ever going to pack the dishes and blankets and sheets they've told us to bring with us?" Keiko worried.

11   "I don't really know," Mama said, and she simply began packing those big impossible things into an enormous duffel bag—along with umbrellas, boots, a kettle, hot plate, and flashlight.

12   "Who's going to carry that huge sack?" I asked.

13   But Mama didn't worry about things like that. "Someone will help us," she said. "Don't worry." So I didn't.

14   Laurie wanted me to open her package and put on the bracelet before she left. It was a thin gold chain with a heart dangling on it. She helped me put it on, and I told her I'd never take it off, ever.

15   "Well, goodbye then," Laurie said awkwardly. "Come home soon."

16   "I will," I said, although I didn't know if I would ever get back to Berkeley again.

17   I watched Laurie go down the block, her long blond pigtails bouncing as she walked. I wondered who would be sitting in my desk at Lincoln Junior High now that I was gone. Laurie kept turning and waving, even walking backward for a while, until she got to the corner. I didn't want to watch anymore, and I slammed the door shut.

18   The next time the doorbell rang, it was Mrs. Simpson, our other neighbor. She was going to drive us to the Congregational Church, which was the Civil Control Station where all the Japanese of Berkeley were supposed to report.

wilt•ed (wil´ təd) *adj.,* falling over; lacking stiffness or shape

FIRST READ ➤

Make Connections
How would you feel if your family had to be identified by a number?

for·sak·en (fôr sā´ kən) *adj.*, abandoned; left

bay·o·net (bā´ ə nət) *n.*, steel blade often attached to the end of a rifle, for use in hand-to-hand fighting

19   It was time to go. "Come on, Ruri. Get your things," my sister called to me.

20   It was a warm day, but I put on a sweater and my coat so I wouldn't have to carry them, and I picked up my two suitcases. Each one had a tag with my name and our family number on it. Every Japanese family had to register and get a number. We were Family Number 13453.

21   Mama was taking one last look around our house. She was going from room to room, as though she were trying to take a mental picture of the house she had lived in for fifteen years, so she would never forget it.

22   I saw her take a long last look at the garden that Papa loved. The irises beside the fish pond[4] were just beginning to bloom. If Papa had been home, he would have cut the first iris blossom and brought it inside to Mama. "This one is for you," he would have said. And Mama would have smiled and said, "Thank you, Papa San"[5] and put it in her favorite cut-glass vase.

23   But the garden looked shabby and forsaken now that Papa was gone and Mama was too busy to take care of it. It looked the way I felt, sort of empty and lonely and abandoned.

24   When Mrs. Simpson took us to the Civil Control Station, I felt even worse. I was scared, and for a minute I thought I was going to lose my breakfast right in front of everybody. There must have been over a thousand Japanese people gathered at the church. Some were old and some were young. Some were talking and laughing, and some were crying. I guess everybody else was scared too. No one knew exactly what was going to happen to us. We just knew we were being taken to the Tanforan Racetracks,[6] which the army had turned into a camp for the Japanese. There were fourteen other camps like ours along the West Coast.

25   What scared me most were the soldiers standing at the doorway of the church hall. They were carrying guns with mounted bayonets. I wondered if they thought we would try to run away and whether they'd shoot us or come after us with their bayonets if we did.

---

4. **irises beside the fish pond.** Elements of a traditional Japanese garden
5. **Papa San.** Japanese term of respect for a father
6. **Tanforan Racetracks.** Assembly area where many Japanese were taken temporarily before being moved to camps

26   A long line of buses waited to take us to camp. There were trucks, too, for our baggage. And Mama was right; some men were there to help us load our duffel bag. When it was time to board the buses, I sat with Keiko, and Mama sat behind us. The bus went down Grove Street and passed the small Japanese food store where Mama used to order her bean-curd cakes and pickled radish. The windows were all boarded up, but there was a sign still hanging on the door that read, "We are loyal Americans."

27   The crazy thing about the whole evacuation was that we were all loyal Americans. Most of us were citizens because we had been born here. But our parents, who had come from Japan, couldn't become citizens because there was a law that prevented any Asian from becoming a citizen.[7] Now everybody with a Japanese face was being shipped off to concentration camps.

28   "It's stupid," Keiko muttered as we saw the racetrack looming up beside the highway. "If there were any Japanese spies around, they'd have gone back to Japan long ago."

29   "I'll say," I agreed. My sister was in high school and she ought to know, I thought.

30   When the bus turned into Tanforan, there were more armed guards at the gate, and I saw barbed wire strung around the entire grounds. I felt as though I were going to a prison, but I hadn't done anything wrong.

31   We streamed off the buses and poured into a huge room, where doctors looked down our throats and peeled back our eyelids to see if we had any diseases. Then we were given our housing assignments. The man in charge gave Mama a slip of paper. We were in Barrack[8] 16, Apartment 40.

32   "Mama!" I said. "We're going to live in an apartment!" The only apartment I had ever seen was the one my piano teacher

FIRST READ

Use Reading Skills
Evaluate Author's Purpose What do these details suggest about the author's purpose?

School children, Manzanar Relocation Center, California. Ansel Adams. Library of Congress.

---

7. **law that prevented any Asian from becoming a citizen.** People of Japanese descent born in the United States became citizens, but Japanese who emigrated to the United States after 1907 were barred from citizenship.
8. **barrack.** Any basic temporary housing

lived in. It was in an enormous building in San Francisco, with an elevator and thick-carpeted hallways. I thought how wonderful it would be to have our own elevator. A house was all right, but an apartment seemed elegant and special.

33   We walked down the racetrack, looking for Barrack 16. Mr. Noma, a friend of Papa's, helped us carry our bags. I was so busy looking around I slipped and almost fell on the muddy track. Army barracks had been built everywhere, all around the racetrack and even in the center oval.

34   Mr. Noma pointed beyond the track toward the horse stables. "I think your barrack is out there."

35   He was right. We came to a long stable that had once housed the horses of Tanforan, and we climbed up the wide ramp. Each stall had a number painted on it, and when we got to 40, Mr. Noma pushed open the door.

36   "Well, here it is," he said, "Apartment 40."

37   The stall was narrow and empty and dark. There were two small windows on each side of the door. Three folded army cots were on the dust-covered floor, and one light bulb dangled from the ceiling. That was all. This was our apartment, and it still smelled of horses.

38   Mama looked at my sister and then at me. "It won't be so bad when we fix it up," she began. "I'll ask Mrs. Simpson to send me some material for curtains. I could make some cushions too, and...well..." She stopped. She couldn't think of anything more to say.

39   Mr. Noma said he'd go get some mattresses for us. "I'd better hurry before they're all gone." He rushed off. I think he wanted to leave so that he wouldn't have to see Mama cry. But he needn't have run off, because Mama didn't cry. She just went out to borrow a broom and began sweeping out the dust and dirt. "Will you girls set up the cots?" she asked.

40   It was only after we'd put up the last cot that I noticed my bracelet was gone. "I've lost Laurie's bracelet!" I screamed. "My bracelet's gone!"

41   We looked all over the stall and even down the ramp. I wanted to run back down the track and go over every inch of ground we'd walked on, but it was getting dark and Mama wouldn't let me.

42   I thought of what I'd promised Laurie. I wasn't ever going to take the bracelet off, not even when I went to take a shower.

SECOND READ

Analyze Literature
Theme What do these details tell you about how the Japanese were treated?

Close Reading

And now I had lost it on my very first day in camp. I wanted to cry.

43   I kept looking for it all the time we were in Tanforan. I didn't stop looking until the day we were sent to another camp, called Topaz, in the middle of a desert in Utah. And then I gave up.

44   But Mama told me never mind. She said I didn't need a bracelet to remember Laurie, just as I didn't need anything to remember Papa or our home in Berkeley or all the people and things we loved and had left behind.

45   "Those are things we can carry in our hearts and take with us no matter where we are sent," she said.

46   And I guess she was right. I've never forgotten Laurie, even now. ♣

SECOND READ

Analyze Literature
Theme In what ways do these final lines help you understand the story's theme?

Mirrors & Windows

How does "The Bracelet" make you feel about the internment of the Japanese during World War II? How might a fictional account help readers relate to a harsh historical event?

Find Meaning	Make Judgments
1. (a) Why is the narrator's family packing their belongings? (b) How do their friends and neighbors react?	**4.** What is the government's attitude toward Ruri's family and other families like them? List details from the story that show this attitude.
2. (a) How much can the family take with them? (b) What will happen to everything else?	**5.** (a) How does Ruri's mother react to what is happening to the family? (b) Do you think she sets a good example for her children? Why or why not?
3. Describe the family's apartment at Tanforan. How do the details about life at Tanforan provide insight about the author's purpose and the story's theme?	**6.** The author could have told the story without mentioning the bracelet. Why do you think the bracelet is in the story?

Analyze Literature

Theme The main topic or focus of "The Bracelet" is the internment of Japanese Americans during World War II. What is the author saying about this topic? Use an organizer like this one to record attitudes toward the internment that the story shows. Then state the theme.

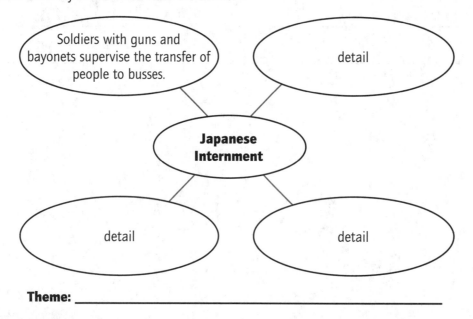

Theme: _____

Writing Connection

Argumentative Writing Imagine that you are a non-Japanese citizen living on the West Coast in 1942 and you're seeing your friends and neighbors marched away to camps. Write an **editorial** for your local newspaper in which you take a stand against the internment of Japanese Americans. Be sure to support your opinion with reasons and explanations.

FIRST READING Key Ideas and Details – What the text says

Build Background

You need to apply two types of background to read a piece of nonfiction effectively. One is the selection's historical, scientific, or cultural context. The other type of background is the personal knowledge you bring to your reading.

Set Purpose

A nonfiction writer writes to inform, describe, persuade, or entertain. Preview the text to find out what you want to learn more about or what questions you have about the topic.

Make Connections

Notice where connections can be made between the information presented in the selection and your life.

Use Reading Skills

Apply close reading skills such as determining author's purpose and using context clues. Make predictions about the text based on the author's use of the features, characteristics, and structures of nonfiction writing. Identify a graphic organizer that will help you apply the skill before and while you read.

SECOND READING Craft and Structure – How the text says it

Reread

Once you have completed the first reading, it is time to go back and reread sections that you didn't understand.

- Ask questions about things that seem significant or interesting to clarify meaning.
- Make inferences, or educated guesses, about what is not stated directly. Reflect on and adjust your responses as new information is presented.

Analyze Literature

A nonfiction writer uses different techniques depending on the type of nonfiction he or she is writing. What literary elements stand out? As you read, consider how these elements affect your enjoyment and understanding of the selection.

Use Text Organization

Determine the structure of the text and how it is organized.

- Break the text down or "chunk" the text into smaller sections to check your comprehension.
- Stop at the end of paragraphs or sections to summarize what you have read.

Unpack Language

Use context clues, along with the margin definitions and footnotes to unpack the language. What is the effect of the author's vocabulary and the language choices he or she makes?

THIRD READING Integration of Knowledge and Ideas – What the text means

Find Meaning

Recall the important details of the selection, such as the sequence of events and settings. Ask questions about the text, using this information to interpret, or explain, the meaning of the selection.

Make Judgments

Analyze the text by examining details and deciding what they contribute to the meaning. Evaluate the text by making judgments about how the author creates meaning and synthesize information to create new understanding.

Analyze Literature

Review how the use of literary elements increased your understanding of the selection. For example, did the author use sensory details or supporting evidence? How did they help shape meaning?

Extend Understanding

Go beyond the text by exploring the selection's ideas through writing, discussion, or other collaborative projects.

The Jacket page 197

MEMOIR by Gary Soto

Build Background

Literary Context Although "The Jacket" reads like a short story, it is actually a memoir, a true story about something that happened to the author when he was in fifth and sixth grade. An autobiographical memoir is a primary, or eyewitness, account of events in the author's life and how he or she felt about them.

Reader's Context How does wearing a favorite item of clothing affect you? How could your clothes influence the way you experience events?

_____

_____

Set Purpose

Preview the memoir's title and first paragraph. As you read, look for ways Soto uses humor to reveal how the events affected him.

Analyze Literature

Memoir A **memoir** is a piece of nonfiction writing that tells a story from the writer's life. Memoirs are about a person's experiences and reactions to historical events. As you read "The Jacket," decide whether Gary Soto is using the memoir to tell about his own experiences or about a historical event that he lived through. Does knowing that the events actually happened to the writer make the story funnier or more interesting to you?

Use Reading Skills

Identify Sequence of Events Using a graphic organizer can help you achieve your purpose in reading. Identifying the sequence of events in a story can help you better understand the plot and allows you to analyze the possible meanings of the events. Create a story strip to record the events in the order in which they happened. Note that not all story events are of equal importance in the plot. Decide which events are significant enough to be recorded.

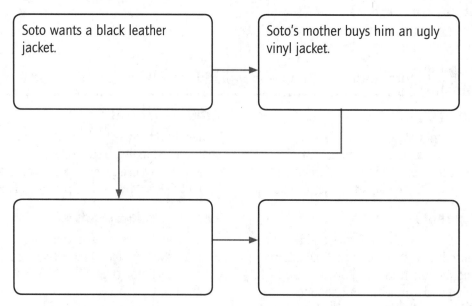

Soto wants a black leather jacket. → Soto's mother buys him an ugly vinyl jacket. →

A Memoir by by Gary Soto

The Jacket

1 My clothes have failed me. I remember the green coat that I wore in fifth and sixth grades when you either danced like a champ or pressed yourself against a greasy wall, bitter as a penny toward the happy couples.

2 When I needed a new jacket and my mother asked what kind I wanted, I described something like bikers wear: black leather and silver studs[1] with enough belts to hold down a small town. We were in the kitchen, steam on the windows from her cooking. She listened so long while stirring dinner that I thought she understood for sure the kind I wanted. The next day when I got home from school, I discovered draped on my bedpost a jacket the color of day-old guacamole.[2] I threw my books on the bed and approached the jacket slowly, as if it were a stranger whose hand I had to shake. I touched the <u>vinyl</u> sleeve, the collar, and peeked at the mustard-colored lining.

3 From the kitchen mother yelled that my jacket was in the closet. I closed the door to her voice and pulled at the rack of clothes in the closet, hoping the jacket on the bedpost wasn't for me but my mean brother. No luck. I gave up. From my bed, I stared at the jacket. I wanted to cry because it was so ugly and so big that I knew I'd have to wear it a long time. I was a small kid, thin as a young tree, and it would be years before I'd have a new one. I stared at the jacket, like an enemy, thinking bad things before I took off my old jacket whose sleeves climbed halfway to my elbow.

4 I put the big jacket on. I zipped it up and down several times, and rolled the cuffs up so they didn't cover my hands. I put my hands in the pockets and flapped the jacket like a bird's wings. I stood in front of the mirror, full face, then profile, and then looked over my shoulder as if someone had called me. I sat on the bed, stood against the bed, and combed my hair to see what I would look like doing something natural. I looked ugly. I threw it on my brother's bed and looked at it for a long time before I slipped it on and went out to the backyard, smiling a "thank you" to my mom as I passed her in the kitchen. With my hands in my pockets I kicked

SECOND READ

Analyze Literature
Memoir From what point of view is this memoir written?

vi•nyl (vī´ n'l) *adj.*, tough, shiny plastic

FIRST READ

Use Reading Skills
Visualize What sensory details does the author use to evoke a mental picture of the jacket?

---

1. studs. Nails with large heads
2. guacamole. Dip or spread made from mashed avocado with spices

swoop (swüp) v., descend quickly in a sweeping movement

SECOND READ

Analyze Literature
Tone Tone is the author's attitude toward the subject. What tone does Soto use when describing how he was treated on the playground?

FIRST READ

Make Connections
How does this description affect your feelings about the narrator?

a ball against the fence, and then climbed it to sit looking into the alley. I hurled orange peels at the mouth of an open garbage can and when the peels were gone I watched the white puffs of my breath thin to nothing.

5   I jumped down, hands in my pockets, and in the back-yard on my knees I teased my dog, Brownie, by <u>swooping</u> my arms while making bird calls. He jumped at me and missed. He jumped again and again, until a tooth sunk deep, ripping an L- shaped tear on my left sleeve. I pushed Brownie away to study the tear as I would a cut on my arm. There was no blood, only a few loose pieces of fuzz. Dumb dog, I thought, and pushed him away hard when he tried to bite again. I got up from my knees and went to my bedroom to sit with my jacket on my lap, with the lights out.

6   That was the first afternoon with my new jacket. The next day I wore it to sixth grade and got a D on a math quiz. During the morning recess Frankie T., the playground terrorist, pushed me to the ground and told me to stay there until recess was over. My best friend, Steve Negrete, ate an apple while looking at me, and the girls turned away to whisper on the monkey bars. The teachers were no help: they looked my way and talked about how foolish I looked in my new jacket. I saw their heads bob with laughter, their hands half-covering their mouths.

7   Even though it was cold, I took off the jacket during lunch and played kickball in a thin shirt, my arms feeling like Braille[3] from goose bumps. But when I returned to class I slipped the jacket on and shivered until I was warm. I sat on my hands, heating them up, while my teeth chattered like a cup of crooked dice. Finally warm, I slid out of the jacket but a few minutes later put it back on when the fire bell rang. We paraded out into the yard where we, the sixth graders, walked past all the other grades to stand against the back fence. Everybody saw me. Although they didn't say out loud, "Man, that's ugly," I heard the buzz-buzz of gossip and even laughter that I knew was meant for me.

8   And so I went, in my guacamole-colored jacket. So embarrassed, so hurt, I couldn't even do my homework. I received Cs on quizzes, and forgot the state capitals and the rivers of South America, our friendly neighbor. Even the girls who had

---

3. Braille. System of writing for the blind that uses raised dots

Close Reading

been friendly blew away like loose flowers to follow the boys in neat jackets.

9   I wore that thing for three years until the sleeves grew short and my forearms stuck out like the necks of turtles. All during that time no love came to me—no little dark girl in a Sunday dress she wore on Monday. At lunchtime I stayed with the ugly boys who leaned against the chainlink fence and looked around with propellers[4] of grass spinning in our mouths. We saw girls walk by alone, saw couples, hand in hand, their heads like bookends pressing air together. We saw them and spun our propellers so fast our faces were blurs.

10   I blame that jacket for those bad years. I blame my mother for her bad taste and her cheap ways. It was a sad time for the heart. With a friend I spent my sixth-grade year in a tree in the alley, waiting for something good to happen to me in that jacket, which had become the ugly brother who tagged along wherever I went. And it was about that time that I began to grow. My chest puffed up with muscle and, strangely, a few more ribs. Even my hands, those fleshy hammers, showed bravely through the cuffs, the fingers already hardening for the coming fights. But that L-shaped rip on the left sleeve got bigger, bits of stuffing coughed out from its wound after a hard day of play. I finally Scotch-taped it closed, but in rain or cold weather the tape peeled off like a scab and more

---

4. propellers. Gadgets with blades that spin around and move a ship or aircraft forward

vi•cious (vi′ shəs) *adj.*, cruel, fierce

mope (mōp) *v.*, be gloomy or in low spirits

stuffing fell out until that sleeve shriveled into a palsied[5] arm. That winter the elbows began to crack and whole chunks of green began to fall off. I showed the cracks to my mother, who always seemed to be at the stove with steamed-up glasses, and she said that there were children in Mexico who would love that jacket. I told her that this was America and yelled that Debbie, my sister, didn't have a jacket like mine. I ran outside, ready to cry, and climbed the tree by the alley to think bad thoughts and watch my breath puff white and disappear.

11   But whole pieces still casually flew off my jacket when I played hard, read quietly, or took <u>vicious</u> spelling tests at school. When it became so spotted that my brother began to call me "camouflage,"[6] I flung it over the fence into the alley. Later, however, I swiped the jacket off the ground and went inside to drape it across my lap and <u>mope</u>.

12   I was called to dinner: steam silvered my mother's glasses as she said grace; my brother and sister with their heads bowed made ugly faces at their glasses of powdered milk. I gagged too, but eagerly ate big rips of buttered tortilla[7] that held scooped-up beans. Finished, I went outside with my jacket across my arm. It was a cold sky. The faces of clouds were piled up, hurting. I climbed the fence, jumping down with a grunt. I started up the alley and soon slipped into my jacket, that green ugly brother who breathed over my shoulder that day and ever since. ❖

---

5. **palsied.** Unable to move
6. **camouflage.** Color pattern of green and brown shades designed to blend in with the background, often used in military clothing and equipment
7. **tortilla.** Round, thin, flat bread usually eaten with meat or cheese

Mirrors & Windows

In this story, Soto says he blames the ugly jacket "for those bad years." Think of a time when you have felt that a situation or experience would have been better if only one thing had been different. Why do you think we allow ourselves to believe that about our pasts?

_____

_____

_____

_____

Find Meaning	Make Judgments
1. (a) What kind of jacket does the narrator want? (b) How does the jacket he receives compare to the jacket he wanted?	**3.** (a) Why do you think the narrator teases his dog? (b) Does teasing Brownie help the situation? Explain.
2. (a) List some of the unfortunate things that happen to the narrator during the years he wears the jacket. (b) How many of these things does the jacket cause?	**4.** Why doesn't the narrator tell his mother that he does not like the jacket?
	5. At the end of the memoir, how have the narrator's feelings about the jacket changed?

Analyze Literature

Memoir In autobiographical writing, an author uses tone and word choice to express his or her feelings. How does Soto's use of humor affect the tone of this memoir? Use a cluster chart to record specific details or examples of Soto's word choice that contribute to the tone. Record each detail or example in the outer circles, and write in the center what you think is the overall tone.

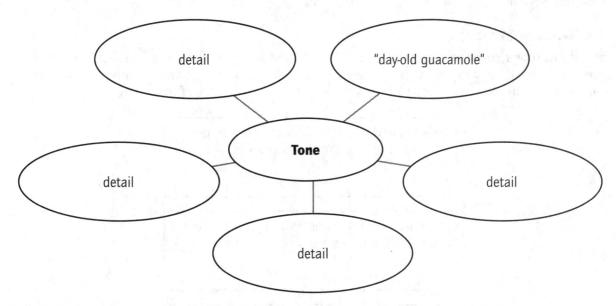

Writing Connection

Informative Writing "The Jacket" vividly re-creates events in Soto's life and reveals his personal feelings. Write a **literary analysis** of how Soto's tone in this memoir reveals his true feelings about that time in his life. Support your thesis with details from your cluster chart.

Abd al-Rahman Ibrahima page 204

BIOGRAPHY by Walter Dean Myers

Build Background

Historical Context Between 1619 and 1865, thousands of Africans were captured and shipped to North America to work as slaves. Living and working conditions for slaves were inhumane, and the slaves spent their nights and days at the hands of cruel and uncaring white slave masters. By 1865, when slavery was finally outlawed, there were four million slaves in the United States. The biography of Abd al-Rahman Ibrahima is the story of just one of the Africans forced into slavery.

Reader's Context Imagine returning to your homeland after being away for most of your life. What do you imagine would have changed?

_____

_____

Analyze Literature

Biography A **biography** is a nonfiction story of a person's life written by another person. A biography is written from the third-person point of view. Sometimes the writer knows the person he or she is writing about. If not, he or she must rely on two types of sources. Primary sources are eyewitness accounts. Secondary sources are those that are based on information from other sources instead of firsthand experience.

Set Purpose

As you read about the events of Ibrahima's early days in Africa, predict what will happen to him in each phase of his life.

Use Reading Skills

Identify Author's Purpose Authors write for different purposes. Some write to entertain. Others write to inform, to persuade, or to explain. In some cases, the author may have more than one purpose. As you read, think about the author's goals. Then write your thoughts before, during, and after reading.

Before Reading: Identify the author's purpose, the type of writing, and the ideas he or she wants to communicate.

During Reading: Gather ideas that the author communicates to readers.

After Reading: Summarize and explain the ideas the author communicates. Explain how these ideas help fulfill the author's purpose.

A Biography by Walter Dean Myers

Abd al-Rahman Ibrahima

1 *Who were these Africans being brought to the New World? What was their African world like? There is no single answer. The Africans came from many countries, and from many cultures. Like the Native Americans, they established their territories based on centuries of tradition. Most, but not all, of the Africans who were brought to the colonies came from central and west Africa. Among them was a man named Abd al-Rahman Ibrahima.*

2 The European invaders, along with those Africans who cooperated with them, had made the times dangerous. African nations that had lived peacefully together for centuries now eyed each other <u>warily</u>. Slight insults led to major battles. Bands of outlaws roamed the countryside attacking the small villages, kidnapping those unfortunate enough to have wandered from the protection of their people. The stories that came from the coast were frightening. Those kidnapped were taken to the sea and sold to whites, put on boats, and taken across the sea. No one knew what happened then.

3 Abd al-Rahman Ibrahima was born in 1762 in Fouta Djallon, a district of the present country of Guinea. It is a beautiful land of green mountains rising majestically from grassy plains, a land rich with minerals, especially bauxite.[1]

4 Ibrahima was a member of the powerful and influential Fula people and a son of one of their chieftains. The religion of Islam[2] had swept across Africa centuries before, and the young Ibrahima was raised in the tradition of the Moslems.

5 The Fula were taller and lighter in complexion than the other inhabitants of Africa's west coast; they had silky hair, which they often wore long. A pastoral[3] people, the Fula had a complex system of government, with the state divided into nine provinces and each province divided again into smaller districts. Each province had its chief and its subchiefs.

6 As the son of a chief Ibrahima was expected to assume a role of political leadership when he came of age. He would also be expected to set a moral example, and to be well

---

FIRST READ

Use Reading Skills
Identify Author's Purpose
What does this introduction suggest about the author's purpose?

war•i•ly (wer´ i lē) *adv.*, carefully; with caution

SECOND READ

Analyze Literature
Point of View From what point of view is this biography written? What clues help you decide?

SECOND READ

Analyze Literature
Biography What information in this paragraph could be checked in another source?

---

1. **bauxite.** Type of ore containing aluminum
2. **Islam.** Second largest religion in the world, founded by Muhammad in ad 622
3. **pastoral.** Relating to animal herding or the countryside

---

des•tined (des´ tənd) *adj.*, decided in advance

SECOND READ ▶

Analyze Literature
Biography What details help you picture how Timbuktu looked in the 1700s?

FIRST READ ▶

Use Reading Skills
Identify Author's Purpose
Why does the author give such a detailed description of Ibrahima's studies?

versed in his religion. When he reached twelve he was sent to Timbuktu[4] to study.

7   Under the Songhai dynasty leader Askia the Great, Timbuktu had become a center of learning and one of the largest cities in the Songhai Empire.[5] The young Ibrahima knew he was privileged to attend the best-known school in west Africa. Large and sophisticated, with wide, tree-lined streets, the city attracted scholars[6] from Africa, Europe, and Asia. Islamic law, medicine, and mathematics were taught to the young men <u>destined</u> to become the leaders of their nations. It was a good place for a young man to be. The city was well guarded, too. It had to be, to prevent the chaos[7] that, more and more, dominated[8] African life nearer the coast.

8   Ibrahima learned first to recite from the Koran, the Moslem holy book, and then to read it in Arabic. From the Koran, it was felt, came all other knowledge. After Ibrahima had finished his studies in Timbuktu, he returned to Fouta Djallon to continue to prepare himself to be a chief.

9   The Fula had little contact with whites, and what little contact they did have was filled with danger. So when, in 1781, a white man claiming to be a ship's surgeon stumbled into one of their villages, they were greatly surprised.

10   John Coates Cox hardly appeared to be a threat. A slight man, blind in one eye, he had been lost for days in the forested regions bordering the mountains. He had injured his leg, and it had become badly infected as he tried to find help. By the time he was found and brought to the Fula chiefs, he was more dead than alive.

11   Dr. Cox, an Irishman, told of being separated from a hunting party that had left from a ship on which he had sailed as ship's surgeon. The Fula chief decided that he would help Cox. He was taken into a hut, and a healer was assigned the task of curing his infected leg.

12   During the months Dr. Cox stayed with the Fula, he met Ibrahima, now a tall, brown-skinned youth who had reached manhood. His bearing[9] reflected his status as the son of a major chief. Dr. Cox had learned some Fulani, the Fula language, and the two men spoke. Ibrahima was doubtless

---

5. **Songhai Empire.** Important empire in western Sudan during the fifteenth and sixteenth centuries
6. **scholars.** Serious students
7. **chaos.** State of confusion
8. **dominated.** Ruled or controlled
9. **bearing.** Way a person holds himself or herself

Close Reading

View of part of the town of Timbuktu taken from a hill to the east, from *Voyage a Tombouctou*, 1830. Rene Caillie. Bibliotheque Nationale, Paris, France.

curious about the white man's world, and Dr. Cox was as impressed by Ibrahima's education as he had been by the kindness of his people.

13   When Dr. Cox was well enough to leave, he was provided with a guard; but before he left, he warned the Fula about the danger of venturing[10] too near the ships that docked off the coast of Guinea. The white doctor knew that the ships were there to take captives.

14   Cox and Ibrahima embraced fondly and said their good-byes, thinking they would never meet again.

15   Ibrahima married and became the father of several children. He was in his mid-twenties when he found himself leading the Fula cavalry in their war with the Mandingo.[11]

16   The first battles went well, with the enemy retreating before the advancing Fula. The foot warriors attacked first, breaking the enemy's ranks and making them easy prey for the well-trained Fula cavalry. With the enemy in full rout[12] the infantry returned to their towns while the horsemen, led by Ibrahima, chased the remaining stragglers. The Fula fought their enemies with spears, bows, slings, swords, and courage.

17   The path of pursuit led along a path that narrowed sharply as the forests thickened. The fleeing warriors disappeared into the forest that covered a sharply rising mountain. Thinking the enemy had gone for good, Ibrahima felt it would be useless to chase them further.

10. **venturing.** Going out
11. **Mandingo.** People of West Africa descended from the people of the ancient Empire of Mali
12. **in full rout.** Fleeing as quickly as possible

FIRST READ

Make Connections
How would it feel if a friend moved so far away that you probably would never see each other again?

SECOND READ

Analyze Literature
Biography How does the author know what Ibrahima was thinking?

18   "We could not see them," he would write later.

19   But against his better judgment, he decided to look for them. The horsemen dismounted at the foot of a hill and began the steep climb on foot. Halfway up the hill the Fula realized they had been lured into a trap! Ibrahima heard the rifles firing, saw the smoke from the powder and the men about him falling to the ground, screaming in agony.[13] Some died instantly. Many horses, hit by the gunfire, thrashed about in pain and panic. The firing was coming from both sides, and Ibrahima ordered his men to the top of the hill, where they could, if time and Allah permitted it, try a charge using the speed and momentum of their remaining horses.

20   Ibrahima was among the first to mount, and urged his animal onward. The enemy warriors came out of the forests, some with bows and arrows, others with muskets that he knew they had obtained from the Europeans. The courage of the Fula could not match the fury of the guns. Ibrahima called out to his men to save themselves, to flee as they could. Many tried to escape, rushing madly past the guns. Few survived.

21   Those who did clustered about their young leader, determined to make one last, desperate stand. Ibrahima was hit in the back by an arrow, but the aim was not true and the arrow merely cut his broad shoulder. Then something smashed against his head from the rear.

22   The next thing Ibrahima knew was that he was choking. Then he felt himself being lifted from water. He tried to move his arms, but they had been fastened securely behind his back. He had been captured.

23   When he came to his full senses, he looked around him. Those of his noble cavalry who had not been captured were already dead. Ibrahima was unsteady on his legs as his clothes and sandals were stripped from him. The victorious Mandingo warriors now pushed him roughly into file with his men. They began the long trek that would lead them to the sea.

24   In Fouta Djallon being captured by the enemy meant being forced to do someone else's bidding, sometimes for years. If you could get a message to your people, you could, perhaps, buy your freedom. Otherwise, it was only if you were well liked, or if you married one of your captor's women, that you would be allowed to go free, or to live like a free person.

25   Ibrahima sensed that things would not go well for him.

---

13. agony. Severe pain and suffering

SECOND READ

Analyze Literature
Biography Does the writer side with the Fula or the Mandingo? What details helped you decide this?

26   The journey to the sea took weeks. Ibrahima was tied to other men, with ropes around their necks. Each day they walked from dawn to dusk. Those who were slow were knocked brutally to the ground. Some of those who could no longer walk were speared and left to die in agony. It was the lucky ones who were killed outright if they fell.

27   When they reached the sea, they remained bound hand and foot. There were men and women tied together. Small children clung to their mothers as they waited for the boats to come and the bargaining to begin.

28   Ibrahima, listening to the conversations of the men who held him captive, could understand those who spoke Arabic. These Africans were a low class of men, made powerful by the guns they had been given, made evil by the white man's goods. But it didn't matter who was evil and who was good. It only mattered who held the gun.

29   Ibrahima was inspected on the shore, then put into irons and herded into a small boat that took him out to a ship that was larger than any he had ever seen.

30   The ship onto which Ibrahima was taken was already crowded with black captives. Some shook in fear; others, still tied, fought by hurling their bodies at their captors. The beating and the killing continued until the ones who were left knew that their lot was hopeless.

31   On board the ship there were more whites with guns, who shoved them toward the open hatch.[14] Some of the Africans

FIRST READ

Use Reading Skills
Identify Author's Purpose
Why does the writer describe what happened to Africans who were captured by other Africans?

---

13. **agony.** Severe pain and suffering
14. **hatch.** Opening into the quarters below deck on a ship

Slaves are shackled and brought below deck on a slave ship in Africa bound for the Americas. Wood engraving, 19th century.

Analyze Literature
Biography What primary sources might Myers have used to research such details?

hesitated at the hatch, and were clubbed down and pushed below decks.

32   It was dark beneath the deck, and difficult to breathe. Bodies were pressed close against other bodies. In the section of the ship he was in, men prayed to various gods in various languages. It seemed that the whites would never stop pushing men into the already crowded space. Two sailors pushed the Africans into position so that each would lie in the smallest space possible. The sailors panted and sweated as they untied the men and then chained them to a railing that ran the length of the ship.

33   The ship rolled against its mooring[15] as the anchor was lifted, and the journey began. The boards of the ship creaked and moaned as it lifted and fell in the sea. Some of the men got sick, vomiting upon themselves in the wretched darkness. They lay cramped, muscles aching, irons cutting into their legs and wrists, gasping for air.

34   Once a day they would be brought out on deck and made to jump about for exercise. They were each given a handful of either beans or rice cooked with yams[16] and water from a cask. The white sailors looked hardly better than the Africans, but it was they who held the guns.

35   Illness and the stifling conditions on the ships caused many deaths. How many depended largely on how fast the ships could be loaded with Africans and how long the voyage from Africa took. It was not unusual for 10 percent of the Africans to die if the trip took longer than the usual twenty-five to thirty-five days.

|||||||||||||

36   Ibrahima, now twenty-six years old, reached Mississippi in 1788. As the ship approached land, the Africans were brought onto the deck and fed. Some had oil put on their skins so they would look better; their sores were treated or covered with pitch.[17] Then they were given garments to wear in an obvious effort to improve their appearance.

37   Although Ibrahima could not speak English, he understood he was being bargained for. The white man who stood on the platform with him made him turn around, and several other white men neared him, touched his limbs, examined his teeth, looked into his eyes, and made him move about.

Use Reading Skills
Make Inferences How did the captured Africans look by the end of the voyage?

---

15. **mooring.** Place where a ship can be docked and tied up
16. **yams.** Root vegetables much like sweet potatoes

Close Reading

© Carnegie Learning, Inc.

38   Thomas Foster, a tobacco grower and a hard-working man, had come from South Carolina with his family and had settled on the rich lands that took their minerals from the Mississippi River. He already held one captive, a young boy. In August 1788 he bought two more. One of them was named Sambo, which means "second son." The other was Ibrahima.

39   Foster agreed to pay $930 for the two Africans. He paid $150 down and signed an agreement to pay another $250 the following January and the remaining $530 in January of the following year.

40   When Ibrahima arrived at Foster's farm, he tried to find someone who could explain to the white man who he was—the son of a chief. He wanted to offer a ransom for his own release, but Foster wasn't interested. He understood, perhaps from the boy whom he had purchased previously, that this new African was claiming to be an important person. Foster had prob-ably never heard of the Fula or their culture; he had paid good money for the African, and wasn't about to give him up. Foster gave Ibrahima a new name: He called him Prince.

41   For Ibrahima there was confusion and pain. What was he to do? A few months before, he had been a learned man and a leader among his people. Now he was a captive in a strange land where he neither spoke the language nor understood the customs. Was he never to see his family again? Were his sons forever lost to him?

42   As a Fula, Ibrahima wore his hair long; Foster insisted that it be cut. Ibrahima's clothing had been taken from him, and his sandals. Now the last remaining symbol of his people, his long hair, had been taken as well.

43   He was told to work in the fields. He refused, and he was tied and whipped. The sting of the whip across his naked flesh was terribly painful, but it was nothing like the pain he felt within. The whippings forced him to work.

44   For Ibrahima this was not life, but a mockery of life. There was the waking in the morning and the sleeping at night; he worked, he ate, but this was not life. What was more, he could not see an end to it. It was this feeling that made him attempt to escape.

45   Ibrahima escaped to the backwoods regions of Natchez.[18] He hid there, eating wild berries and fruit, not daring to show

SECOND READ

Analyze Literature
Biography How does the writer connect Ibrahima's life in Africa with his life in the New World?

SECOND READ

Analyze Literature
Biography What primary source might have provided Myers with these chilling details?

17. **pitch.** Sticky sap from a pine tree
18. **Natchez.** City on the Mississippi River in 1716 in what is now the state of Mississippi

his face to any man, white or black. There was no telling who could be trusted. Sometimes he saw men with dogs and knew they were searching for runaways, perhaps him.

46   Where was he to run? What was he to do? He didn't know the country, he didn't know how far it was from Fouta Djallon, or how to get back to his homeland. He could tell that this place was ruled by white men who held him in captivity. The other blacks he had seen were from all parts of Africa. Some he recognized by their tribal markings, some he did not. None were allowed to speak their native tongues around the white men. Some already knew nothing of the languages of their people.

Use Reading Skills
Identify Author's Purpose
Why does the writer explain the reasons behind Ibrahima's decision?

bond•age (bän´ dij) *n.,* slavery

47   As time passed Ibrahima's despair deepened. His choices were simple. He could stay in the woods and probably die, or he could submit his body back into <u>bondage</u>. There is no place in Islamic law for a man to take his own life. Ibrahima returned to Thomas Foster.

48   Foster still owed money to the man from whom he had purchased Ibrahima. The debt would remain whether he still possessed the African or not. Foster was undoubtedly glad to see that the African had returned. Thin, nearly starving, Ibrahima was put to work.

49   Ibrahima submitted himself to the will of Thomas Foster. He was a captive, held in bondage not only by Foster but by the society in which he found himself. Ibrahima maintained his beliefs in the religion of Islam and kept its rituals[19] as best he could. He was determined to be the same person as he had always been: Abd al-Rahman Ibrahima of Fouta Djallon and of the proud Fula people.

SECOND READ

Analyze Literature
Tone What details tell you how Myers feels about Ibrahima?

50   By 1807 the area had become the Mississippi Territory. Ibrahima was forty-five and had been in bondage for twenty years. During those years he met and married a woman whom Foster had purchased, and they began to raise a family. Fouta Djallon was more and more distant, and he had become resigned to the idea that he would never see it or his family again.

51   Thomas Foster had grown wealthy and had become an important man in the territory. At forty-five Ibrahima was considered old. He was less useful to Foster, who now let the tall African grow a few vegetables on a side plot and sell them in town, since there was nowhere in the territory that the

---

19. rituals. Ceremonies that are repeated in a culture and imbued with meaning

black man could go where he would not be captured by some other white man and returned.

52 It was during one of these visits to town that Ibrahima saw a white man who looked familiar. The smallish man walked slowly and with a limp. Ibrahima cautiously approached the man and spoke to him. The man looked closely at Ibrahima, then spoke his name. It was Dr. Cox.

53 The two men shook hands and Dr. Cox, who now lived in the territory, took Ibrahima to his home. John Cox had not <u>prospered</u> over the years, but he was still hopeful. He listened carefully as Ibrahima told his story—the battle near Fouta Djallon, the defeat, the long journey across the Atlantic Ocean, and, finally, his sale to Thomas Foster and the years of labor.

54 Dr. Cox and Ibrahima went to the Foster plantation. Meeting with Foster, he explained how he had met the tall black man. Surely, he reasoned, knowing that Ibrahima was of royal blood, Foster would free him? The answer was a firm, but polite, no. No amount of pleading would make Foster change his mind. It didn't matter that Dr. Cox had supported what Ibrahima had told Foster so many years before, that he was a prince. To Foster the man was merely his property.

55 Dr. Cox had to leave the man whose people had saved his life, but he told Ibrahima that he would never stop working for his freedom.

56 Andrew Marschalk, the son of a Dutch baker, was a printer, a pioneer in his field, and a man of great curiosity. By the time Marschalk heard about it, Cox had told a great many people in the Natchez district the story of African royalty being held in slavery in America. Marschalk was fascinated. He suggested that Ibrahima write a letter to his people, telling them of his whereabouts and asking them to ransom him. But Ibrahima had not been to his homeland in twenty years. The people there were still being captured by slave traders. He would have to send a messenger who knew the countryside, and who knew the Fula. Where would he find such a man?

57 For a long time Ibrahima did nothing. Finally, some time after the death of Dr. Cox in 1816, Ibrahima wrote the letter that Marschalk suggested. He had little faith in the procedure but felt he had nothing to lose. Marschalk was surprised when Ibrahima appeared with the letter written neatly in Arabic. Since one place in Africa was the same as the next

FIRST READ

Make Connections
How would you feel if you unexpectedly ran into an old friend you had not seen in many years?

pros•per (präs´ pər) v., succeed, do well

SECOND READ

Analyze Literature
Biography What source would most likely have this type of information?

Analyze Literature
Biography Would Ibrahima's letter be a primary or a secondary source? Why?

prem•ise (prem′ əs) *n.*, idea on which an argument is based

FIRST READ

Use Reading Skills
Identify Author's Purpose What does Myers's tone regarding the idea of slavery suggest about his purpose?

SECOND READ

Analyze Literature
Biography Does this biography tell the entire life of Ibrahima, or is it only about one part of his life?

FIRST READ

Use Reading Skills
Identify Author's Purpose Do you think the author achieved his purpose in this selection? Explain your answer.

to Marschalk, he sent the letter not to Fouta Djallon but to Morocco.

58   The government of Morocco did not know Ibrahima but understood from his letter that he was a Moslem. Moroccan officials, in a letter to President James Monroe, pleaded for the release of Ibrahima. The letter reached Henry Clay, the American Secretary of State.

59   The United States had recently ended a bitter war with Tripoli in north Africa, and welcomed the idea of establishing good relations with Morocco, another north African country. Clay wrote to Foster about Ibrahima.

60   Foster resented the idea of releasing Ibrahima. The very idea that the government of Morocco had written to Clay and discussed a religion that Ibrahima shared with other Africans gave Ibrahima a past that Foster had long denied, a past as honorable as Foster's. This idea challenged a basic premise of slavery—a premise that Foster must have believed without reservation: that the Africans had been nothing but savages, with no humanity or human feelings, and therefore it was all right to enslave them. But after more letters and pressure from the State Department, Foster agreed to release Ibrahima if he could be assured that Ibrahima would leave the country and return to Fouta Djallon.

61   Many people who believed that slavery was wrong also believed that Africans could not live among white Americans. The American Colonization Society had been formed expressly to send freed Africans back to Africa. The society bought land, and a colony called Liberia was established on the west coast of Africa. Foster was assured that Ibrahima would be sent there.

62   By then Ibrahima's cause had been taken up by a number of abolitionist[20] groups in the north as well as by many free Africans. They raised money to buy his wife's freedom as well.

63   On February 7, 1829, Ibrahima and his wife sailed on the ship *Harriet* for Africa. The ship reached Liberia, and Ibrahima now had to find a way to reach his people again. He never found that way. Abd al-Rahman Ibrahima died in Liberia in July 1829.

64   Who was Ibrahima? He was one of millions of Africans taken by force from their native lands. He was the son of a

---

20. abolitionist. Person who favored ending slavery

chief, a warrior, and a scholar. But to Ibrahima the only thing that mattered was that he had lost his freedom. If he had been a herder in Fouta Djallon, or an artist in Benin, or a farmer along the Gambia, it would have been the same. Ibrahima was an African who loved freedom no less than other beings on earth. And he was denied that freedom. ♣

Mirrors & Windows

What about Abd al-Rahman Ibrahima's story affected you the most? Why? Do you think the United States should help people in other countries win freedom from cruel leaders and undemocratic governments?

_____

_____

_____

_____

Find Meaning	**Make Judgments**
1. (a) Who is the subject of this biography? (b) Why do you think the author chose to write about him?	**4.** Why did a brave man like Ibrahima submit to working for Thomas Foster?
2. (a) Who captures Ibrahima? (b) Where do they take him?	**5.** (a) Why do you think that Ibrahima hesitated before writing a letter about his problem for Marschalk? (b) Why do you think he changed his mind after Dr. Cox died?
3. (a) Why does Thomas Foster buy Ibrahima? (b) What is Ibrahima expected to do for Thomas Foster? (c) How does he react to his new job?	**6.** Do you think Ibrahima would have made a good leader for his people? Explain.

Analyze Literature

Biography How does the chronological organization of this biography help unify Ibrahima's story? Create a time line to help determine the chain of events that made up Ibrahima's life. Record as many dates as you can identify with the corresponding events. How do the events in Africa affect Ibrahima's reaction to the events in Natchez?

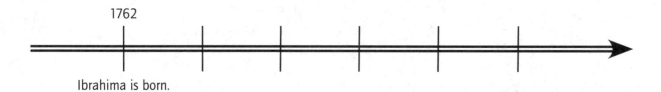

1762

Ibrahima is born.

Writing Connection

Informative Writing Using your time line, write a brief **summary** of this biography, including important facts and events, as well as the author's theme. Make sure you do not include opinions in your summary. Be sure to summarize and synthesize the selection in ways that maintain meaning and logical order within the text.

 page 219

PERSONAL ESSAY by Anne Frank

Build Background

Historical Context Anne Frank was a Jewish teenager in Germany when Adolf Hitler and his Nazi Party rose to power. Hitler blamed Germany's problems on the Jewish people and set out to destroy Europe's Jewish population. In 1933, Anne Frank's family fled to Holland. There they lived in hidden rooms for two years before they were discovered and sent to a concentration camp.

Reader's Context Think of the different types of questions you ask. Do all questions have good answers?

_____

_____

Analyze Literature

Personal Essay A **personal essay** is a nonfiction work on a single topic related to the life of the writer. Like any good essay, a personal essay develops a single idea, or **thesis**. As you read, think about Anne Frank's **thesis** and how she supports it with examples from her own life.

Set Purpose

Preview the Historical Context. Based on these facts and the selection title, make a list of four questions you might have for Anne Frank before reading her essay with a goal of gaining information and deepening understanding.

Use Reading Skills

Context Clues Try to unlock the meaning of each vocabulary word using the context clues provided in the sentences.

1. "If you <u>badger</u> Mom with your constant whining, she'll never say yes," said Ray.

_____

2. My friends <u>consoled</u> me when my pet bird died.

_____

3. After losing the race, José revealed his strong <u>character</u> by warmly congratulating the winner.

_____

4. Julia's <u>conscience</u> told her it was wrong to cheat on the test.

_____

5. Instead of yelling, we talked and resolved our differences <u>reasonably</u>.

_____

A Personal Essay by Anne Frank

Why?

1 The little word "why" has been a very strong thing with me ever since I was a tiny little girl and couldn't even speak properly. It is a well-known fact that little children ask questions about everything because they are unfamiliar with everything. This was very much the case with me, but even when I grew older I couldn't wait to ask all kinds of questions, whether they could be answered or not. This is not so terrible in itself and I must say that my parents tried to answer every one of my questions very patiently, until...I began even <u>badgering</u> strangers, and they generally can't stand "children's endless questions." I must admit that this can be very tiresome, but I <u>console</u> myself with the idea that there is a saying that "you must ask in order to know," which couldn't be completely true, otherwise I'd be a professor[1] by now.

2 When I grew older, I realized that it is not possible to ask every kind of question to everyone and that there are many "why's" that cannot be answered. It then followed from that that I tried to help myself by starting to think out these questions on my own. So I came to the important discovery that questions which one mustn't ask can be solved by oneself. Therefore, the little word "why" taught me not only to ask but to think.

3 Now as to the second part of the word "why." How would it be if everyone who did anything asked himself first, "Why?"

Anne Frank writing at her desk in her house at Merwedeplein, c. 1941.

---

1. professor. Teacher in a university or college

I think they would then become more honest and much, much better people. For the best way to become honest and good is to keep examining oneself without stopping. I can imagine that the last thing people like to do is to confess to themselves their faults and their bad side (which everybody has). This is the case with children as well as grownups—in that respect I don't see any difference. Most people think parents should try to educate their children and see to it themselves that their <u>characters</u> develop as well as possible. This is certainly untrue. Children ought to educate themselves from their earliest youth and must try to show real character by themselves. Many will think this is crazy, but it isn't. Even a very small child is a little personality and has a <u>conscience</u> and should be brought up by being treated in this way, so that it will feel that its own conscience is punishing it in the harshest way possible. When children reach the age of fourteen or fifteen, every punishment is ridiculous. Such a child knows very well that no one, not even its own parents, can get anywhere with punishments and spankings. By arguing <u>reasonably</u> and by showing the child the mistakes it is making, one would get much better results than by strong punishments.

4   But here, I don't want to sound pedantic,[2] but only to say that in the life of every child and every man, the little word "why" plays a big part, and rightly so. The saying, "You must ask in order to know," is true in so far as it leads to thinking about things, and by thinking nobody can ever get worse but will only get better. ♣

char·ac·ter (ker´ ik tər) *n.*, person's behavior, thoughts, and personality

con·science (kän[t]´ shən[t]s) *n.*, thoughts and feelings about right and wrong

rea·son·a·bly (rē´ z'n ə blē) *adv.*, agreeably, logically

---

2. pedantic. Characterized by too much attention paid to unimportant details

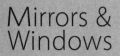
Mirrors & Windows

Think of a time when asking yourself "why" before doing something might have resulted in a better decision. What would you have done differently? How might the world be better if everyone did this?

_____

_____

_____

_____

Find Meaning	Make Judgments
1. (a) How did Anne learn about her world? (b) What kind of personality did Anne have?	**5.** (a) How can a person's conscience punish him or her? (b) Why might reasonable arguments be more effective than punishments?
2. What does Anne Frank believe should be encouraged and developed in children?	**6.** Do you agree with Anne's statements about asking questions and learning? Why or why not?
3. According to Anne, to what does the act of asking questions lead?	**7.** Identify literary devices used in this selection.
4. (a) According to Anne, how can asking "why" make you a better person? (b) Do you agree with her? Explain.	

Analyze Literature

Personal Essay A **personal essay** must have a **thesis,** or main idea. What might be the thesis of "Why?" How does Anne Frank develop her thesis with details and examples? Use a main idea map to record the components of this personal essay. Skim the essay for the most important details and examples to record in the outer ovals of the map. Analyze those details to determine the thesis and write it in the center oval.

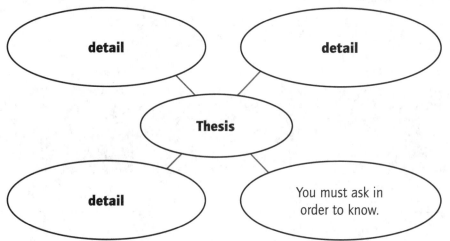

Writing Connection

Argumentative Writing Create a main idea map of the most important thing you think parents must do in raising children. Put your main idea in the middle. Think of at least four supporting examples. Using your map, write **an argumentative paragraph** convincing parents to do this thing. State your main idea in your thesis.

from All I Really Need to Know I Learned in Kindergarten page 224

`ARGUMENTATIVE ESSAY` by Robert Fulghum

Build Background

Literary Context When authors want to persuade a reader of something, they often use examples from their own lives to evoke emotion. Robert Fulghum's essay uses imagery and examples from the games of hide-and-seek and Sardines in order to describe and persuade. When he writes about hiding or about piling together like sardines, Fulghum is trying to uncover a larger truth about the way people interact with each other.

Reader's Context What kinds of things have you "hid" in order to keep them secret? How do you feel after sharing them?

_____

_____

Analyze Literature

Argumentative Essay An **argumentative essay** is written to promote an opinion. The **thesis** is the author's opinion, or argument. An argumentative essay supports the thesis with examples. Fulghum describes human behavior by making comparisons between hide-and-seek and keeping secrets, and between Sardines and sharing your troubles with others.

Set Purpose

Preview the first paragraph and predict what Fulghum wants his reader to feel or think.

Use Reading Skills

Analyze Author's Perspective Using a graphic organizer can help you understand how the details in an argumentative essay connect to an author's perspective—the point of view or position the author takes. Create a chart to organize the details of the essay. In the first column, write details that seem important. In the second column, write down what each detail tells you about the author's beliefs.

Details	Beliefs
The author shouts at the kid hiding under his window.	People shouldn't hide from others.

Close Reading Model

An Argumentative Essay by Robert Fulghum

from All I Really Need to Know I Learned in Kindergarten

FIRST READ

Use Reading Skills
Visualize Imagine this kind of weather at this time of day. What might the weather tell you about the writer's mood?

SECOND READ

Use Reading Skills
Analyze Author's Perspective What does the author's emphasis of certain words tell you about how he wants you to read those words?

con·sid·er (kən siˊ dər) *v.*, think carefully about something

1 In the early dry dark of an October's Saturday evening, the neighborhood children are playing hide-and-seek. How long since I played hide-and-seek? Thirty years; maybe more. I remember how. I could become part of the game in a moment, if invited. Adults don't play hide-and-seek. Not for fun, anyway. Too bad.

2 Did you have a kid in your neighborhood who always hid so good, nobody could find him? We did. After a while we would give up on him and go off, leaving him to rot wherever he was. Sooner or later he would show up, all mad because we didn't keep looking for him. And we would get mad back because he wasn't playing the game the way it was supposed to be played. There's *hiding* and there's *finding*, we'd say. And he'd say it was hide-and-seek, not hide-and-give-UP, and we'd all yell about who made the rules and who cared about who, anyway, and how we wouldn't play with him anymore if he didn't get it straight and who needed him anyhow, and things like that. Hide-and-seek-and-yell. No matter what, though, the next time he would hide too good again. He's probably still hidden somewhere, for all I know.

3 As I write this, the neighborhood game goes on, and there is a kid under a pile of leaves in the yard just under my window. He has been there a long time now, and everybody else is found and they are about to give up on him over at the base. I considered going out to the base and telling them where he is hiding. And I thought about setting the leaves on fire to drive him out. Finally, I just yelled, "GET FOUND, KID!" out the window. And scared him so bad he probably wet his pants and started crying and ran home to tell his mother. It's real hard to know how to be helpful sometimes.

4 A man I know found out last year he had terminal cancer.[1] He was a doctor. And knew about dying, and he didn't want to make his family and friends suffer through that with him. So he kept his secret. And died. Everybody said how brave he was to bear his suffering in silence and not tell everybody, and so on and so forth. But privately his family and friends said

---

1. **terminal cancer.** Illness that spreads through the body, resulting in death

Close Reading

how angry they were that he didn't need them, didn't trust their strength. And it hurt that he didn't say good-bye.

5   He hid too well. Getting found would have kept him in the game. Hide-and-seek, grown-up style. Wanting to hide. Needing to be sought.[2] Confused about being found. "I don't want anyone to know." "What will people think?" "I don't want to bother anyone."

6   Better than hide-and-seek, I like the game called Sardines.[3] In Sardines the person who is It goes and hides, and everybody goes looking for him. When you find him, you get in with him and hide there with him. Pretty soon everybody is hiding together, all stacked in a small space like puppies in a pile. And pretty soon somebody giggles and somebody laughs and everybody gets found.

7   Medieval[4] theologians even described God in hide-and-seek terms, called him *Deus Absconditus*.[5] But me, I think old God is a Sardine player. And will be found the same way everybody gets found in Sardines—by the sound of laughter of those heaped together at the end.

8   "Olly-olly-oxen-free."[6] The kids out in the street are hollering the cry that says "Come on in, wherever you are. It's a new game." And so say I. To all those who have hid too good. *Get found, kid!* Olly-olly-oxen-free. ♣

---

2. **sought.** Past tense of the verb *seek*, meaning "to look for"
3. **sardines.** Small fish that are tightly packed in metal containers
4. **medieval.** From a period in European history between the fifth and early fifteenth centuries
5. *Deus Absconditus.* Latin term for a hidden god
6. **olly-olly-oxen-free.** Phrase used in a game of hide-and-seek to indicate that people who are hiding can safely come out

FIRST READ

Make Connections
How is keeping an important secret like hiding?

the·o·lo·gian
(thē′ ə lō′ jən) *n.*, expert in the study of religion

SECOND READ

Analyze Literature
Persuasive Essay What does the writer want to persuade his reader to feel, think, or do?

Mirrors & Windows

Many children have played games of hide-and-seek. Have you ever hid in a different way? Did someone "find" you? Why might some problems seem easier to fix when there are others around?

_____

_____

_____

_____

Find Meaning	Make Judgments
1. (a) How long has it been since Fulghum played hide-and-seek? (b) How does he say adults "play" hide-and-seek?	**4.** (a) Why does Fulghum want the kid outside his window to be found? (b) How is the kid like the man with cancer?
2. What happens in Fulghum's description of his childhood games of hide-and-seek?	**5.** (a) Which game, hide-and-seek or Sardines, does Fulghum say is better? (b) What is his evidence?
3. (a) How does Fulghum end the game of hide-and-seek happening outside his window? (b) What are the things Fulghum considers doing to make the kid "get found"?	**6.** Does Fulghum's description of Sardines as hiding in "a small space like puppies in a pile" persuade you to feel a certain way about the game? Describe that feeling.
	7. (a) To whom is Fulghum speaking at the beginning of the essay? (b) To whom is he speaking at the end?

Analyze Literature

Argumentative Essays Argumentative essays use a combination of emotion- and logic-based details. Emotion-based details appeal to a reader's feelings. Logic-based details appeal to a reader's idea of what makes sense and provide evidence to support the argument. How does Fulghum appeal to your emotions? How does he appeal to your logic? Skim the essay for emotional appeals versus logical appeals. Use a chart to make a list of all the evidence you find. At the bottom, write what you think is the thesis of the essay.

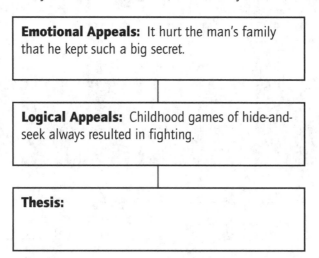

Emotional Appeals: It hurt the man's family that he kept such a big secret.

Logical Appeals: Childhood games of hide-and-seek always resulted in fighting.

Thesis:

Writing Connection

Informative Writing Many readers of Robert Fulghum's writing feel persuaded by its simple reflections because it connects to their lives. Write a paragraph in which you conduct a **literary analysis** of the essay. In your thesis, state whether or not you felt Fulghum's essay was effective. Explain why or why not. Provide two or three reasons as support. Compare your analysis with those of your classmates.

Unit 4

The Five "Wanderers" of the Ancient Skies page 284

SCIENTIFIC ARTICLE by Dennis Brindell Fradin

Build Background

Scientific Context The five "wanderers" of this essay are objects that move in the night sky. People in most ancient cultures developed stories to explain what they saw in the sky. Today we know that stars create their own light, and planets reflect the light from stars. We also know that planets orbit stars in paths determined by gravity, and moons orbit planets.

Reader's Context Have you ever seen a shooting star? Have you wondered why the moon changes shape over the course of a month?

Analyze Literature

Informational Text Science and culture often overlap. This article gives a scientific perspective on some cultural traditions. As you read, think about what you have learned previously about outer space, stars, and the solar system.

Set Purpose

Preview the article by skimming it for proper nouns, especially capitalized words inside sentences. Then predict one or two things you might learn from the article. Read the article to see if your predictions are correct.

Use Reading Skills

Take Notes This article includes a great deal of information about ancient cultures, plus historical ideas of how the solar system works. Keep track of details with a chart. For each page, list details that seem significant or interesting. After you finish reading the article, review your notes and write one or two main ideas for each section or page.

Section or Page	Interesting Details	Main Ideas
p. 86	• Moon cycles on bones • No change in star positions	Some space objects move more than others.

A Scientific Article by Dennis Brindell Fradin

The Five "Wanderers" of the Ancient Skies

Aristarchus was accused of evil teachings. He refused to acknowledge that the Earth is at the center of the Universe. Instead, he claimed that it moves in an orbit [around the Sun] and at the same time spins on its axis.

—Ancient description of the Greek astronomer Aristarchus, who lived about 2,300 years ago

1   On a clear night, in a place far from city lights, a person with good vision can see about 3,000 stars in the sky. A few stars are so bright that they dazzle the eye, but many others are barely visible. There are white stars and blue stars, orange stars and red stars, yellow stars and stars that seem to change color as they twinkle. Many people who view the starfilled sky for the first time are almost hypnotized by its splendor. Whether children or adults, they are likely to wonder: How many stars are there and how far away are they? Do stars extend forever in space or is there a place where they end? Are we alone in the Universe, or do beings on other worlds look up at their night sky with the same sense of awe that we feel?

2   People have undoubtedly asked these questions for most of our two million years on Earth. Some of the oldest known relics created by human beings have astronomical significance. Ten thousand-year-old bones on which people recorded the cycles of the Moon have been found in Africa and Europe. Cliff drawings and stone monuments found in many places also prove that people have been intrigued by the objects in the heavens since prehistoric times.

3   Our ancient ancestors observed that seven celestial[1] objects behave differently than the stars in the night sky. One of them, the huge yellow orb we call the Sun, appears only by day and seems to take the light away when it sets each evening. The second unusual object was the large body we call the Moon, which seems to change shape during a cycle lasting about thirty days.

4   The other five unusual objects resemble bright stars, yet differ from them in two important ways. First, a star twinkles

in·trigue (in trēg´) *v.*, fascinate, interest

rel·ic (re´ lik) *n.*, artifact

---

1. celestial. Relating to the sky, outer space, or heaven

"like a diamond in the sky," as the nursery rhyme says, while the five special objects shine with a steady light. Also, the relative positions of the stars change so slowly over long periods of time that the ancients made up imaginary star pictures called constellations that look nearly the same today as they did thousands of years ago. On the other hand, the five unusual objects do not remain in fixed positions, but move through the constellations from month to month and year to year.

5   Ancient people generally worshiped the seven unusual heavenly bodies as gods and goddesses. The Greeks believed that the Sun was the god Helios and the Moon his sister Selene. They referred to the five bright objects that moved among the constellations as *planetae,* meaning "wanderers." Although the Greeks did not understand the nature of the "wanderers," their word *planetae* lives on in our modern name for the objects: *planets.*

6   The Romans coined the names still applied to the five known planets of ancient times. The fast-moving orange planet that always remained near the Sun they named *Mercury,* for their fleet-footed messenger of the gods who wore magic sandals. The brilliant white planet that outshone every heavenly body except the Sun and the Moon they called *Venus,* for their goddess of love. The red planet reminded the Romans of blood, so they named it *Mars,* for their god of war. The yellow planet that wandered slowly through the constellations the Romans named *Jupiter,* for their king of the gods who was also known as Jove. The golden planet that moved even more slowly than Jupiter they named *Saturn,* for Jupiter's father. The Romans worshiped the Moon as Luna, a goddess who drove across the night sky in her chariot, and identified the Sun with Apollo, the god of musicians and poets.

7   Other people had their own beliefs about the seven special heavenly bodies. To the people of ancient India the Sun was Surya, a god who was driven across the sky by a seven-headed horse. The ancient Egyptians believed that the planets Mars, Jupiter, and Saturn were various forms of Horus, a god with a man's body and a bird's head. The Babylonians, who lived in what is now Iraq, worshiped Jupiter as Marduk, their king of the gods who killed a dragon and created the sky and the oceans out of its body. Mexico's Maya and Aztec Indians referred to Venus as Quetzalcoatl, a god who also took the form of a feathered serpent. The Masai people of Africa

FIRST READ

Use Reading Skills
Take Notes How do these five objects differ from stars?

FIRST READ

Use Reading Skills
Take Notes What names did the Romans give to five of today's planets?

as·so·ci·ate (ə sō′ shē āt′) *v.,* connect

claimed that the Sun and the Moon were a husband and wife who had a fight. The Sun god was so ashamed of his bruises that he made himself bright to keep people from looking at him, but when we gaze upon the Moon goddess's face, we can see her injuries.

8   Ancient Jewish people did not <u>associate</u> the heavenly bodies with gods and goddesses, for their religion, Judaism, taught that there is only one God. Yet they believed that each planet influenced a part of the human body and a day of the week. For example, Mars was associated with the right ear and the day we call Tuesday, and Mercury's influence extended to the left nostril and Friday. The Chinese identified each planet with an important substance. They called Mercury *Shui Xing,* the Water Star, and Venus *Jin Xing,* the Gold Star. The red planet, Mars, was *Huo Xing,* the Fire Star, while Jupiter was *Mu Xing,* the Wood Star, and Saturn was *Tu Xing,* the Earth Star.

9   The Moon, Sun, and five planets known to the ancients influenced our language, calendar, and other aspects of our daily life. Seven is considered a lucky number to this day because of the seven unusual heavenly bodies, and the week has seven days for the same reason. Each of our days is named for one of the objects. *Sunday* and *Monday* are old words meaning "the Sun's Day" and "the Moon's Day." *Tuesday, Wednesday,* and *Thursday* come from old words meaning "the Day of Mars," "the Day of Mercury," and "the Day of Jupiter." *Friday* is "the Day of Venus," and *Saturday* is "Saturn's Day."

10   Helium, an element used to fill balloons, was named for the Sun god, Helios. Because the god and planet Mercury moved so quickly, the element used in thermometers was named mercury, and individuals whose moods quickly change are called "mercurial." People who are gloomy or slow to act are sometimes described as "saturnine" for the slow-moving planet, while good-natured individuals are called "jovial" in honor of Saturn's son, King Jupiter or Jove. Long ago, nations took time out from wars during the winter, because the cold weather could claim more lives than the battles. They resumed fighting when the weather turned warmer, which was why the first month of spring was named *March* for Mars, the god of war.

11   The Moon inspired the custom of dividing the year into twelve segments. Each of these periods roughly corresponds to the Moon's thirty-day cycle and is called a *month,* a word related to *Mene,* meaning "Moon" in Greek. The Moon also figures in many old superstitions, including the belief that

Astronomical chart showing a swan, a lyre, a lizard, and a fox killing a goose, forming the constellations Lacerta, Cygnus, Lyra, Vulpecula, and Anser.

it could transform people into werewolves or wolf-men. To this day, mentally ill people are sometimes called *lunatics,* as a result of the ancient belief that the Moon and its goddess, Luna, could do strange things to the human mind.

12 Except for a handful of individuals considered in their own time to be lunatics, ancient people shared a completely false view of the Universe. They thought that all of the heavenly bodies circled the Earth, which stood motionless at the center of everything. There seemed to be a simple "proof" of this. At night the Moon, stars, and planets traveled across the sky in an arc from east to west, and each day the Sun did the same. All a person had to do was watch a planet rise over a treetop in the east or a star set behind a mountain in the west to see "evidence" that the heavenly bodies circled the Earth from east to west.

SECOND READ

Analyze Literature
Informational Text How does the author judge this ancient view of the universe? How does he characterize people who held a different view?

13 The Greek astronomer Aristarchus was one of the very few ancient scientists who differed with this theory. About 2,300 years ago, Aristarchus claimed that the heavenly bodies only *appear* to circle overhead because our Earth spins like a top. He also suggested that the Earth orbits the Sun—not the other way around. Aristarchus was accurate on both counts, but for many centuries his ideas were ridiculed.

14 Ptolemy, a Greek astronomer who was born about 100 ad, led the attack on Aristarchus's theories. "If the Earth actually rotated to the east," reasoned Ptolemy, "wouldn't winds always blow westward and clouds always move westward?" Ptolemy

Use Reading Skills
Take Notes Who led the attack on Aristarchus's ideas?

con•coct (kən käkt´) v., create by combining ingredients or ideas

Use Reading Skills
Clarify Based on the word *concocted,* what is the author's opinion of Ptolemy's explanation?

reign (rān) v., rule; exercise power

became the most famous spokesman for the false idea that the Earth stands still and is the center of the Universe, a theory that became known as the "Ptolemaic System." Its followers, called "Ptolemaists," developed numerous arguments to explain why the Earth couldn't possibly spin. One was that a spinning Earth would make us feel constantly dizzy. They also argued that if the Earth really rotated, a rock or ball hurled into the sky would be left far behind rather than coming down near where it was thrown.

15   One thing disturbed the Ptolemaists, however. Certain movements of the planets could best be explained if in fact they orbited the Sun rather than the Earth. At times some planets make backward loops in the sky. This *retrograde motion*[2] is due to the Earth overtaking the other "wanderers" as the planets all orbit the Sun, much as a car traveling 50 miles per hour on a highway can appear to be moving backward if you are whizzing past it at 60 miles per hour. Ptolemy concocted another explanation for the planets' backward loops. He claimed that the planets travel in large circles around the Earth, but that they sometimes also move in extra small circles called *epicycles.* Although completely wrong, this explanation won acceptance because it accounted for the retrograde motion of the "wanderers" while keeping the Earth standing still at the center of the Universe.

16   The Ptolemaic System reigned virtually[3] unchallenged for nearly 1,400 years. During those fourteen centuries the Earth spun like a top (as Aristarchus claimed) half a million times, Mercury orbited the Sun five thousand times, and Saturn made fifty trips around the Sun—yet all the while humanity continued to believe that we stood motionless at the center of creation. ✤

2. **retrograde motion.** Moving in the opposite of the expected direction; backward
3. **virtually.** Almost entirely

Mirrors & Windows

Which explanation for the planets most appeals to you? Do you think there is room in modern society for both scientific and cultural explanations of the planets and stars? Or, should people be required to accept a particular viewpoint of the night sky?

Find Meaning	Make Judgments
1. (a) Ancient people observed seven objects that "behave differently than the stars in the night sky." However, the title of this essay is "The Five 'Wanderers' of the Ancient Skies." What are the five wanderers? (b) Which other two bodies did the ancient people observe?	**4.** (a) What do many of the ancient names for the five wanderers have in common? (b) How did the ancient Jewish explanation of the wanderers differ from other explanations?
2. (a) What are constellations? (b) How do the five wanderers differ from constellations?	**5.** Give at least three examples of how the seven celestial bodies in this article have influenced the language we use every day.
3. For what or whom did ancient Romans name each of the five wanderers?	**6.** (a) Are our modern explanations of the solar system primarily cultural or primarily scientific? (b) How do they compare with the explanations of the past? Explain.

Analyze Literature

Informational Text Analyze Fradin's article with a K-W-L chart. In the first column, put something you already knew about the Sun, Moon, and planets. In the center column, write something you want to learn about them. Scan your notes to remind yourself of key points, and then, in the third column, write what you learned from the article.

What I Already Know	What I Want to Learn	What I Learned
The Sun is the center of our solar system.	Did ancient people know about the solar system?	Some space objects move more than others.

Writing Connection

Creative Writing Close your eyes to visualize the night sky. Imagine that you belong to an ancient African society. Think of a short story you could write about the Moon, Sun, and planets. Then **outline** a plot or draw a **plot diagram** for your story. List your characters and identify the main conflict in the plot. Write down how you would reveal the exposition, the rising action, the climax, the falling action, and the resolution of the plot.

NOISE LEVELS page 298

DIAGRAM by Bob Ludlow

Build Background

Scientific Context Sound is a kind of energy that travels in waves. To produce a sound wave, something has to vibrate—the air and metal in a horn, for example, or a set of human vocal cords. When sound waves enter your ears, the waves vibrate your eardrums. The vibrations move along to various structures and passageways until your ears signal your brain. How loud a sound is—its volume or intensity—depends on the strength of the vibrations that set the sound waves in motion.

Reader's Context How loud is your world? Recall the softest and loudest sounds you've heard so far today. What words would you use to describe how loud they were?

_____

_____

Analyze Literature

Visual Media A diagram should communicate some information without words. Before you study this diagram, look for trends by comparing rows and columns. Note where pieces of visual information seem to overlap or interact. Get an impression of how colors and shapes are used to draw your attention. As you examine the diagram further, find out if your initial impressions were on the right track.

Set Purpose

Preview the diagram. Determine its subject by reading the title and labels. Find how the information is organized. Then, review the sounds you've heard in just the past few minutes and think about what you'd like to learn from the diagram.

Use Reading Skills

Skim and Scan Look at the diagram. As you read, your brain will organize information in the diagram into logical categories that have meaning for you. After you read, you may want to sort the information into new categories for further use. Right now, skim the title and list of sounds on the left side of the diagram. Sketch a chart like this for recording what you learn.

Sounds I Hear		
Often	Rarely	Never
home stereo	rock concert	chain saw

A Diagram by Bob Ludlow

NOISE LEVELS

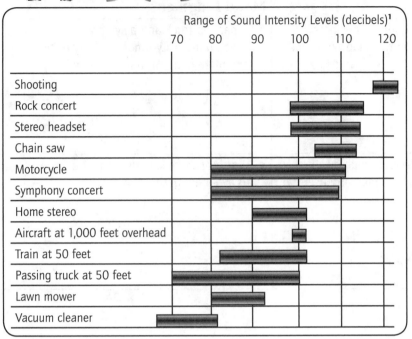

Range of Sound Intensity Levels (decibels)[1]

	70	80	90	100	110	120
Shooting						▬
Rock concert				▬▬▬▬		
Stereo headset				▬▬▬▬		
Chain saw					▬▬	
Motorcycle		▬▬▬▬▬▬▬				
Symphony concert		▬▬▬▬▬▬				
Home stereo			▬▬▬			
Aircraft at 1,000 feet overhead				▪		
Train at 50 feet		▬▬▬▬				
Passing truck at 50 feet	▬▬▬▬▬					
Lawn mower		▬▬▬				
Vacuum cleaner	▬▬					

1. **decibel.** Unit measuring loudness of sounds (volume, intensity); abbreviated *db*

FIRST READ

Reading Skills
Skim and Scan What does each horizontal bar represent?

SECOND READ

Analyze Literature
Visual Media Based on the chart, which sound is the most dangerous to your hearing?

Mirrors & Windows

What sounds in your life damage your hearing the most? How can we teach young children to protect their hearing?

_____

_____

_____

_____

Find Meaning	Make Judgments
1. Sound intensities above eighty-five decibels can be harmful. Which sound on this diagram is *never* harmful?	**3.** A passing truck and a symphony concert both have an intensity range of thirty decibels. Why is one more harmful than the other?
2. (a) What is the smallest decibel range on the diagram? (b) Why is this sound more intense than that of a lawn mower?	**4.** Which of these sounds would be easiest for you to avoid altogether?

The diagram you just interpreted relates to the following article. As you read the article, try to determine the author's purpose. Look for facts and opinions. Determine whether the writer wants to inform, entertain, or persuade you.

NOTES

Hearing Under Siege page 300

MAGAZINE ARTICLE by Bob Ludlow from Cooking Light Magazine

1 Whether it's rock or Bach, music that's played too loud can put more than a temporary damper[1] on your hearing. At most rock concerts and many night clubs, the sound intensity is high enough to cause irreversible damage to the delicate sensor cells lining the inner ear. Car and home stereo equipment and headphones can also harm your hearing when the volume is cranked up too high.

2 Noted noise-pollution expert William Clark, Ph.D., a researcher at the Central Institute for the Deaf, in St. Louis, is especially troubled by reports of teenagers' music listening habits. He cites recent studies of personal stereo use that indicate 5% to 10% of these young people are risking significant hearing loss. In his testimony before Congress, Clark called for mandatory warning labels to be placed on stereo equipment as well as red warnings on volume controls.

3 But loud music is only one of the threats to good hearing that abound[2] in everyday life. Workplace noise has long been recognized as a major cause of permanent hearing loss. And outside of work, many kinds of home and recreational equipment have the potential to damage your hearing. Power saws, leaf blowers, model airplanes, all-terrain vehicles, and firearms—especially firearms—are cause for concern. So are the high noise levels at automobile races, motorcycle races, and other crowded sporting events.

---

1. damper. Device that muffles sound by controlling vibrations
2. abound. Exist in large numbers

Know the Signs

4   Hearing experts recommend a simple "talk test" as a practical means of safeguarding your hearing. They say that the noise level is too high if it's hard to carry on a conversation with someone who is three feet away from you.

5   Experts also tell people to beware of temporary changes in hearing, such as ringing or a "stuffy" feeling in the ears. These symptoms are not just harmless annoyances but signs that the wispy nerve endings called "hair cells" have been traumatized.

How Loud and How Long

6   The intensity, or loudness, of sound is measured in units called decibels. A whisper, which is at the lower end of the scale, registers about 20 decibels, while normal speech comes in at a comfortable 60. Sound begins to get "uncomfortable" at about 70 decibels, and it becomes potentially harmful when it reaches 85 or 90 decibels. A typical rock concert assaults your ears with 100 to 120 decibels.

7   The damage done by noise depends not only on how loud it is but also on the length of time you're exposed to it. Many workers are continuously subjected to levels above 85 decibels on a daily basis. The cumulative effects of high levels of industrial and environmental noise add up to some very alarming statistics.

8   By age 65, for instance, 20% to 30% of the people in the United States will have difficulty hearing normal conversational levels. To reduce the risks to workers, federal agencies as well as private industry have set limits on allowing noise exposure in the workplace. But there are no regulations providing effective protection from everyday noise outside of work.

Bang, Bang, You're Deaf

9   When noise levels are extremely high, severe damage can occur from just a single, brief exposure. Clark puts such risks in perspective by firing off a round of high-powered scientific "ammunition." "A shot from a 357 Magnum (165 decibels) is the acoustic equivalent of working in a noisy factory for a week," he explains. "Firing a box of shells is like working in that same factory for a year. Much of the hearing loss that's been blamed on the workplace actually comes from hunting and target shooting. Our research showed that people who worked in a noisy plant but didn't shoot had better hearing

than a similar group who worked in a quiet office and did shoot."

10 And guns don't have to be real to cause real harm. Children's cap pistols (105 to 125 decibels), when fired close to the ear, are not safe toys.

Sensible Precautions

11 Experts in hearing conservation[3] offer several common sense guidelines that can help you preserve good hearing throughout your lifetime.

- Always wear protective devices, such as earplugs or specially designed earmuffs, when working in noisy settings or with loud equipment.
- Never use firearms without effective hearing protection.
- Spend less time in noisy environments, and give your ears frequent breaks from periods of continuous noise exposure. Consider carrying and using earplugs the way you use sunglasses.

12 The chart on page 93 lists decibel levels for some common activities and equipment. Clark and other experts aren't saying you have to avoid all noisy activities—just be aware of noise levels and take sensible precautions. ❖

What do you think is the purpose of the article? In the past several years, manufacturers of some MP3 players and other audio equipment have started limiting the volume you can get out of the devices. Where does the article or the diagram include information that would support those manufacturers' actions?

_____

_____

_____

_____

Analyze Literature

Visual Media Which did you personally find more useful, the magazine article or the diagram? Think about which version of the information you prefer and imagine some ways you could use the information. What could make the diagram more useful? For example, consider reorganizing the diagram by intensity range, like the example at right. What are some other ways you could present the information?

Comfortable (less than 70 db)	Uncomfortable (70–85 db)	Harmful (more than 85 db)
	vacuum cleaner	chain saw

Writing Connection

Informative Writing Imagine one of your relatives is having trouble hearing what people say at family gatherings. You know he or she used to be in a band that opened for big-name country music performers. Even though it's too late to reverse the hearing loss, you'd like to let the person know you understand the cause of this trouble. Write an **informative** paragraph explaining the possible source of the hearing loss. Use at least one detail from the diagram or the article to support your main idea.

Key Ideas and Details – What the text says

Build Background

You need to apply two different types of background to read a poem effectively. One type is the poem's literary and historical context. The other type of background is the personal knowledge and experience you bring to your reading.

Set Purpose

Set Purpose to decide what you want to get out of the poem. Note who the narrator, or speaker, is in the poem.

Make Connections

Notice where connections can be made between the poem and your life or the world outside the poem. What feelings or thoughts do you have while reading the poem?

Use Reading Skills

Apply close reading skills to poetry, such as identifying the main idea, making inferences, and visualizing. Identify a graphic organizer that will help you apply the skill before and while you read.

Craft and Structure – How the text says it

Text Organization

Determine the structure of the poem and how it is organized.

- How are the lines arranged? Do any words rhyme? How many lines are there in each stanza?
- Pay attention to punctuation and line breaks. Chunk the lines in the poem so they make sense.
- Try reading all the way to the end of the sentence rather than stopping at each line break.
- Stop at the end of stanzas or sections to summarize what you have read.

Analyze Literature

What is the purpose of the poem, and what literary elements achieve that purpose? For example, how does imagery or rhyme add to the meaning? Note how these elements affect your understanding of the poem. Poets use different techniques in writing different poems.

Tackle Vocabulary

Look for context clues in the lines near the word, consult a dictionary, or ask someone about words you do not understand. Use the provided definitions and footnotes.

Integration of Knowledge and Ideas – What the text means

Find Meaning

Reread to recall the important details of the poem, such as the images, figurative language, and rhyme scheme. Use this information to interpret, or explain, the poem's meaning.

Make Judgments

- Analyze the poem by examining details and deciding what they contribute to the meaning.
- Evaluate the poem by making judgments about how the author creates meaning.

Analyze Literature

Review how the use of literary elements increases your understanding of the poem. For example, how might figurative language shape a poem's meaning?

Extend Understanding

Go beyond the text by exploring the poem's ideas through writing, discussion, or other creative projects.

ODE TO LA TORTILLA page 349

NARRATIVE POEM by Gary Soto

Build Background

Literary Context In ancient times, an **ode** was a long, serious, thoughtful poem of praise, usually with irregular stanzas. In the Romantic period, poets such as Keats and Wordsworth penned emotional odes focused on one subject—often something in nature. Keats's "Ode to a Grecian Urn" is one of the most famous poems of this era. Like many odes from the past, Soto's ode focuses on some aspects of nature. Mainly, though, the poem is Soto's song of praise for a special food in his life—the tortilla.

Reader's Context What kind of food would you like to praise? What do you love to eat hot from the oven or the pan?

_____

_____

Analyze Literature

Imagery The use of language to create a concrete representation of an object or an experience is **imagery**. In some cases, an image is a mental picture. In others, it's a smell, taste, or other sensory experience. As you read the poem, notice the sight, sound, touch, and taste images. In addition, notice the poet's use of nature imagery.

Set Purpose

Sensory language is language that creates a mental image by appealing to one or more of the five senses. As you read, think about how the sensory language makes this poem come to life.

Use Reading Skills

Determine Sequence of Events As you read, keep track of the sequence of events the poet describes. Are the events told in the order in which they occurred? How do you know? Pay attention to the tense of the speaker's words. Use a Sequence Chart like the one below to chart the events in the poem in chronological order.

speaker stands on the lawn, eating

↓

speaker throws a piece of tortilla to a sparrow

↓

↓

↓

↓

A Narrative Poem by Gary Soto

ODE TO LA TORTILLA

They are flutes
When rolled, butter
Dripping down my elbow
As I stand on the
5 Front lawn, just eating,
Just watching a sparrow
Hop on the lawn,
His breakfast of worms
Beneath the green, green lawn,
10 Worms and a rip of
Tortilla I throw
At his thorny feet.
I eat my tortilla,
Breathe in, breathe out,
15 And return inside,
Wiping my oily hands
On my knee-scrubbed jeans.
The tortillas are still warm
In a dish towel,
20 Warm as gloves just
Taken off, finger by finger.
Mamá is rolling
Them out. The radio
On the window sings,
25 *El cielo es azul...*[1]
I look in the black pan:
The face of the tortilla
With a bubble of air
Rising. Mamá
30 Tells me to turn
It over, and when
I do, carefully,
It's blistered brown.
I count to ten,

---

1. *El cielo es azul.* The sky is blue (Spanish).

SECOND READ

Analyze Literature
Imagery What do you see on the lawn?

Use Reading Skills
Visualize What does the tortilla look like before and after the speaker flips it?

35 *Uno, dos, tres...*
And then snap it out
Of the pan. The tortilla
Dances in my hands
As I carry it
40 To the drainboard,
Where I smear it
With butter,
The yellow ribbon of butter
That will drip
45 Slowly down my arm
When I eat on the front lawn.
The sparrow will drop
Like fruit
From the tree
50 To stare at me
With his glassy eyes.
I will rip a piece
For him. He will jump
On his food
55 And gargle it down,
Chirp once and fly
Back into the wintry tree. ❧

Analyze Literature
Imagery What might a reader see and hear at the end of the poem?

To what ordinary objects in your life can you imagine writing an ode?
Why does the "ordinary" need to be celebrated?

Find Meaning	Make Judgments
1. Who is the speaker in this poem?	**4.** Which sensory image struck you most as you read this poem? Why?
2. (a) How is the speaker eating the tortillas? (b) Why do you think he emphasizes the way in which he is eating?	**5.** Who or what is being compared in this poem? Cite exact words from the poem in your answer.
3. What does the sparrow do in the poem?	**6.** Would you say this poem is actually about "la tortilla," or something else? Explain.

Analyze Literature

Imagery Go back and reread the scene in the kitchen. How does Gary Soto use imagery to put the reader in the kitchen and to help the reader experience exactly what the speaker experiences? List the images that bring this scene to life. Tell which of your senses each image appeals to. What effect does the imagery have on you?

Image	Sense the Image Appeals To
"The radio on the window sings, `El cielo es azul...'"	hearing

Writing Connection

Narrative Writing "Ode to La Tortilla" can be read as a sequence of events. Rewrite them as a **narrative paragraph**. That is, retell in the first-person point of view what happens in time order. Include all the speaker's actions, as well as the actions of the sparrow. Be sure to use transitional words that show time order, such as *first, next, then, and finally.*

Abuelito Who page 354

LYRIC POEM by Sandra Cisneros

Build Background

Cultural Context *Abuelito* is a Spanish word that comes from the word *abuelo*, meaning "grandfather." The speaker has added the ending -*ito* to make the term more personal and loving. The poem suggests that the speaker and the grandfather speak both English and Spanish.

Reader's Context How would you describe an older family member or friend who is both very sick and very dear to you?

_____

_____

Set Purpose

Preview the poem by looking closely at the art and thinking about the title. Read the first line and predict what the poem will be about. Who do you think is speaking? Read to learn more.

Analyze Literature

Metaphor and Simile A **metaphor** is a figure of speech in which one thing is spoken or written about as if it were another. In other words, a metaphor makes an unusual comparison, such as, "The kite was a boat sailing through the sky." A **simile** is another type of comparison, but it uses the word *like* or *as* to compare. As you read this poem, look for unusual or fresh comparisons. Identify them as either metaphors or similes, and decide what they tell you about Abuelito.

Use Reading Skills

Draw Conclusions To draw conclusions about a poem, look for information from the poem and determine what it means. Draw conclusions to find out about the speaker of the poem. Look at the poetic devices in the poem, such as figurative language and sound devices, to draw conclusions about the poem's meaning. Use a chart like this one to record your questions and possible conclusions.

My Questions	Possible Conclusions
Who is the poem's speaker?	a grandchild is writing about her grandfather
Where is the grandfather?	

Close Reading

A Lyric Poem by Sandra Cisneros

Abuelito Who

Abuelito who throws coins like rain
and asks who loves him
who is dough and feathers
who is a watch and glass of water
5 whose hair is made of fur
is too sad to come downstairs today
who tells me in Spanish you are my diamond
who tells me in English you are my sky
whose little eyes are string
10 can't come out to play
sleeps in his little room all night and day
who used to laugh like the letter k[1]
is sick
is a doorknob tied to a sour stick
15 is tired shut the door
doesn't live here anymore
is hiding underneath the bed
who talks to me inside my head
is blankets and spoons and big brown shoes
20 who snores up and down up and down up and down again
is the rain on the roof that falls like coins
asking who loves him
who loves him who? ❧

---

1. the letter k. Because the letter k is rare in Spanish words, this detail suggests an unusual,
strange, or unnatural-sounding laugh.

SECOND READ

Analyze Literature
Metaphor and Simile Why does the
speaker compare Abuelito to dough and
feathers?

FIRST READ

Use Reading Skills
Draw Conclusions What conclusion can
you draw from line 16?

Mirrors & Windows

What are some of the qualities you love most in the people around you? Are
the traits we find most endearing in other people always strengths, or can
they be weaknesses?

Find Meaning	Make Judgments
1. (a) Where is Abuelito? (b) What is the matter with him?	**4.** (a) What is the speaker feeling? (b) How do you know?
2. (a) What are two things Abuelito is doing now? (b) What are two things Abuelito did in the past?	**5.** How would you describe the relationship between Abuelito and the speaker?
3. (a) Is it true that Abuelito "doesn't live here anymore"? (b) What does that statement suggest?	**6.** Do you think the question in the last line has an answer? If so, what is it? If not, why not?

Analyze Literature

Metaphor and Simile In "Abuelito Who," some of the metaphors and similes help you see Abuelito as the speaker sees him. Use a chart like the one at right to list the comparisons that give you clues about how Abuelito looks as he lies ill in bed. For example, for the metaphor "who is dough and feathers," you might see soft skin and a face that is white like dough. For each comparison you list, explain in your own words what you see.

Comparisons	What I See
a watch and glass of water	items at the side of a sickbed

Writing Connection

Informative Writing Review the chart you created listing the metaphors and similes in "Abuelito Who." Then write a **literary response** to the poem. In your response, include a thesis that states your overall impression of the poem and how the poem's figurative language affected your impression. To support your thesis, quote examples of the most effective figurative language. Explain how each example made you feel, as well as how it helped you understand the emotions of the speaker. Share your responses in small groups, and discuss the different reactions of each reader.

LIFE DOESN'T FRIGHTEN ME page 361

LYRIC POEM by Maya Angelou

Build Background

Literary Context "Life Doesn't Frighten Me" is a poem that uses various elements of traditional verse, such as rhyme and stanzas. Although "Life Doesn't Frighten Me" includes these elements, the rhyme scheme and the lengths of the stanzas vary. The poet unifies, or brings together, the poem by repeating a single line in almost every stanza. The repeated line acts like a musical refrain or chorus.

Reader's Context What are you frightened by? Why?

_____

_____

Set Purpose

Preview the title and first stanza. What tone of voice do you hear? Predict whether the other stanzas will follow in the same tone.

Use Reading Skills

Scan for Repetition Scanning a text means moving your eyes quickly over a page or section in order to find particular information, words, or patterns. Before you begin reading, scan the poem for repeated words and phrases. Note where they appear in the lines and stanzas. Later, determine the effect of the repetition.

Analyze Literature

Rhyme and Repetition The repetition of sounds at the ends of words is **rhyme**. A **rhyme scheme** is the set pattern a poet follows in creating rhyme. A *slant rhyme* exists when two sounds are almost but not exactly alike, like *brave* and *made*. **Repetition** is the repeated use of a sound, word, or group of words. As you read the poem, identify the rhymes and slant rhymes at the ends of lines. Also, look for repetition and determine its effect.

Repeated Word or Phrase	Where It Appears	Effect
life	in the title and at the beginning of several lines	

Close Reading

A Lyric Poem by Maya Angelou

LIFE DOESN'T FRIGHTEN ME

Shadows on the wall
Noises down the hall
Life doesn't frighten me at all
Bad dogs barking loud
5 Big ghosts in a cloud
Life doesn't frighten me at all.

Mean old Mother Goose[1]
Lions on the loose
They don't frighten me at all
10 Dragons breathing flame
On my counterpane[2]
That doesn't frighten me at all.

I go boo
Make them shoo
15 I make fun
Way[3] they run
I won't cry
So they fly
I just smile
20 They go wild
Life doesn't frighten me at all.

Tough guys in a fight
All alone at night
Life doesn't frighten me at all.

25 Panthers in the park
Strangers in the dark
No, they don't frighten me at all.

---

1. **Mother Goose.** Supposed author of well-known children's stories and nursery rhymes dating back to the seventeenth century
2. **counterpane.** Bedspread
3. **way.** Shortened form of *away*

SECOND READ

Analyze Literature
Rhyme and Repetition Identify the words that repeat and the words that rhyme at the ends of lines in this stanza.

FIRST READ

Use Reading Skills
Scan for Repetition Where does the most repetition in the poem occur? What is the effect?

That new classroom where
Boys all pull my hair
30 (Kissy little girls
With their hair in curls)
They don't frighten me at all.

Don't show me frogs and snakes
And listen for my scream.
35 If I'm afraid at all
It's only in my dreams.

I've got a magic charm
That I keep up my sleeve,
I can walk the ocean floor
40 And never have to breathe.

Life doesn't frighten me at all
Not at all
Not at all.
Life doesn't frighten me at all. ❖

FIRST READ

Use Reading Skills
Make Connections How do the speaker's feelings about these things compare to your own?

Mirrors & Windows

What strategies do you use to deal with frightening situations? How do such strategies change as we grow up?

_____

_____

_____

_____

Close Reading

Find Meaning	Make Judgments
1. What are three things that the speaker says do not frighten him or her?	**4.** How would you describe the speaker's attitude toward events in life? Why?
2. What does the speaker do to make frightening things go away?	**5.** (a) Is the speaker ever afraid? (b) How do you know?
3. Identify the speaker. Use details from the poem to support your answer.	**6.** In what ways does this poem seem to be for or about very young children?

Analyze Literature

Rhyme and Repetition Think about the phrase the poet keeps repeating in this poem. Then think about why the speaker chooses to do this in rhymes. What do the repetition and rhyme suggest about the speaker? For example, what do they reveal about the speaker's worries? What do they tell you about the speaker's determination? Make a two-column chart to list the effects of rhyme and repetition in the poem.

Literary Device	Effect
rhyme	
repetition	

Writing Connection

Informative Writing In fiction, authors reveal characters through their words, thoughts, and actions. Poetry usually reveals speakers through their words, thoughts, and tone. Write a **character analysis** of the speaker in "Life Doesn't Frighten Me" to share with a classmate. Write a topic sentence that states one of the speaker's most important character traits. Cite evidence from the poem as support.

The Walrus and the Carpenter page 366

NARRATIVE POEM by Lewis Carroll

Build Background

Literary Context "The Walrus and the Carpenter" is a work of pure fantasy. Fantasy is any story about impossible things—such as a talking walrus or the sun shining brightly in the middle of the night. Some fantasy literature, like this poem, mixes the fantastic with the familiar. This poem is part of a longer novel by Lewis Carroll called *Through the Looking-Glass,* which relates the adventures of Alice, a young, imaginative girl who passes through a mirror into a mysterious, fantastical world.

Reader's Context Have you ever followed along when you shouldn't have? What signs of trouble ahead did you miss?

Analyze Literature

Alliteration The repetition of consonant sounds at the beginning of words or syllables is **alliteration,** as in *bats in the belfry.* Alliteration is a sound device that makes poetry more musical to the ear of the reader or listener. As you read, identify examples of alliteration. Think about how they contribute to the poem's effect.

Set Purpose

Preview the title and the illustrations. Predict what the pair named in the title might do. Then read the first stanza and predict again. Revise your predictions as you read.

Use Reading Skills

Use Context Clues Preview these vocabulary words as they are used in the following sentences. Determine the meaning of each word by looking at the context clues.

1. Dan <u>beseeched</u> his mother to let him attend the party.

2. The fresh clams tasted faintly of the <u>briny</u> ocean water.

3. When Jill poured the root beer over the ice cream, the drink became <u>frothy</u>.

4. Until the <u>dismal</u> weather subsided, the team practiced indoors.

5. "I can't <u>sympathize</u> unless you tell me what's wrong," said Ann.

A Narrative Poem by Lewis Carroll

The Walrus and the Carpenter

The sun was shining on the sea,
    Shining with all his might:
He did his very best to make
    The billows[1] smooth and bright—
5 And this was odd, because it was
    The middle of the night.

The moon was shining sulkily,[2]
    Because she thought the sun
Had got no business to be there
10   After the day was done—
"It's very rude of him," she said,
    "To come and spoil the fun!"

The sea was wet as wet could be,
    The sands were dry as dry.
15 You could not see a cloud because
    No cloud was in the sky:
No birds were flying overhead—
    There were no birds to fly.

The Walrus and the Carpenter
20   Were walking close at hand:
They wept like anything to see
    Such quantities of sand:
"If this were only cleared away,"
    They said, "it *would* be grand!"

25 "If seven maids with seven mops
    Swept it for half a year,
Do you suppose," the Walrus said,
    "That they could get it clear?"
"I doubt it," said the Carpenter,
30   And shed a bitter tear.

FIRST READ

Use Reading Skills
Clarify What time of day is it? What is the setting?

SECOND READ

Analyze Literature
Alliteration Identify the alliteration in lines 19–21.

---

1. billows. Waves
2. sulkily. In a brooding, pouting, or glum and silent manner

be·seech (bi sēch´) v., beg; ask in a begging or urgent way

bri·ny (brī´ nē) adj., salty

"O Oysters, come and walk with us!"
　　The Walrus did <u>beseech</u>.
"A pleasant walk, a pleasant talk,
　　Along the <u>briny</u> beach:
35　We cannot do with more than four,
　　To give a hand to each."

The eldest Oyster looked at him,
　　But never a word he said:
The eldest Oyster winked his eye,
40　　And shook his heavy head—
Meaning to say he did not choose
　　To leave the oyster-bed.

But four young Oysters hurried up,
　　All eager for the treat:
45　Their coats were brushed, their faces washed,
　　Their shoes were clean and neat—
And this was odd, because, you know,
　　They hadn't any feet.

Four other Oysters followed them,
50　　And yet another four;
And thick and fast they came at last,
　　And more, and more, and more—
All hopping through the <u>frothy</u> waves,
　　And scrambling to the shore.

fro·thy (frô´ thē) adj., foamy; full of bubbles

55　The Walrus and the Carpenter
　　Walked on a mile or so,
And then they rested on a rock
　　Conveniently low:
And all the little Oysters stood
60　　And waited in a row.

"The time has come," the Walrus said,
　　"To talk of many things:
Of shoes—and ships—and sealing-wax[3]—
　　Of cabbages—and kings—
65　And why the sea is boiling hot—
　　And whether pigs have wings."

SECOND READ

Analyze Literature
Alliteration How does alliteration help make lines 63–64 stand out?

---

3. **sealing-wax.** Melted candle wax used to seal envelopes

Close Reading

"But wait a bit," the Oysters cried,
　　"Before we have our chat;
For some of us are out of breath,
70　　And all of us are fat!"
"No hurry!" said the Carpenter.
　　They thanked him much for that.

"A loaf of bread," the Walrus said,
　　"Is what we chiefly need:
75　Pepper and vinegar besides
　　Are very good indeed—
Now, if you're ready, Oysters dear,
　　We can begin to feed."

"But not on us!" the Oysters cried,
80　　Turning a little blue.
"After such kindness, that would be
　　A <u>dismal</u> thing to do!"
"The night is fine," the Walrus said.
　　"Do you admire the view?"

dis•mal (diz´ məl) *adj.*, dreadful;
especially bad

Use Reading Skills
Make Predictions Evaluate the Oysters' concern. What do you think is going to happen?

sym•pa•thize
(sim´ pə thīz´) v., share in someone else's trouble or sadness

Make Connections
How do you feel about the poem's ending? Explain your answer.

85   "It was so kind of you to come!
          And you are very nice!"
      The Carpenter said nothing but
          "Cut us another slice.
      I wish you were not quite so deaf—
90   I've had to ask you twice!"

      "It seems a shame," the Walrus said,
          "To play them such a trick.
      After we've brought them out so far,
          And made them trot so quick!"
95   The Carpenter said nothing but
          "The butter's spread too thick!"

      "I weep for you," the Walrus said:
          "I deeply sympathize."
      With sobs and tears he sorted out
100   Those of the largest size,
      Holding his pocket-handkerchief
          Before his streaming eyes.

      "O Oysters," said the Carpenter,
          "You've had a pleasant run!
105   Shall we be trotting home again?"
          But answer came there none—
      And this was scarcely odd, because
          They'd eaten every one. ❖

Mirrors & Windows

How do you feel about the Oysters by the end of the poem? Is their fate justified? When might it be unwise to trust people you don't know?

_____

_____

_____

_____

Close Reading

Find Meaning	Make Judgments
1. Where are the Walrus and the Carpenter?	**4.** At the end of the poem, the Walrus says he sympathizes with the Oysters. Do you think he truly does? Support your opinion with evidence from the text. Reflect on how your opinion after reading lines up with the inferences you made before and during reading. Explain.
2. (a) What causes the Walrus and the Carpenter to weep? (b) Do they see any solution to this problem? Explain.	**5.** What do you think is funny about the poem? Find two examples.
3. (a) Why do most of the Oysters go for a walk with the Walrus and the Carpenter? (b) Why doesn't the eldest Oyster go? (c) What happens to the younger Oysters?	**6.** Do you think the author's purpose was just to be silly, or do you think he had another purpose? Cite words or details in the poem.

Analyze Literature

Alliteration Look back at the third through fifth stanzas of the poem. Identify the uses of alliteration you find. Create a chart listing the alliteration you identify. Explain how each example contributes to the mood of the poem and how it affects you as a reader. Note that repeated words also contribute to alliteration.

Line Numbers	Alliteration	Effect
25-26	"...seven maids with seven mops/ Swept..."	

Writing Connection

Informative Writing How does alliteration affect the overall impact of the poem? Use the alliteration chart you created after reading the selection to organize your thoughts. Write a **literary response** in which you explain how the alliteration affects how you read the poem.

 page 408

LYRIC POEM by Langston Hughes

Build Background

Literary Context Langston Hughes wrote during the Harlem Renaissance, a cultural explosion of art, literature, and music that began in the 1920s. Many African-American writers, artists, and musicians lived and worked in the Harlem neighborhood of New York City at that time. They created art that expressed their pride in African-American culture, causing African Americans to embrace their cultural traditions in spite of the racial prejudice that was common at that time.

Reader's Context Think about some dreams that are important to you. Have you shared those dreams with others? Why or why not?

_____

_____

Analyze Literature

Speaker The **speaker** is the voice that narrates a poem. The speaker and the writer of a poem are not always the same. As you read "The Dream Keeper," decide whether the speaker is the poet. If not, decide who the speaker might be.

Set Purpose

Preview the title of the poem. Make a prediction about who or what a dream keeper might be. To whom might the poet be speaking? Read on to assess your predictions.

Use Reading Skills

Reread Poems often have many layers of meaning. You can reread a poem many times and discover something new about it each time. For example, the first time you read, you may just focus on the main idea. Rereading might help you notice the language and rhythm, grasp deeper themes, and think about how the poem relates to your life. You can use a graphic organizer like the one below to record different things you notice with each rereading of a poem.

Reading	Idea
First	It is important to have and keep dreams.
Second	The phrases "blue cloud-cloth" and "too-rough fingers" are strong contrasts.

A Lyric Poem by Langston Hughes

The Dream Keeper

Bring me all of your dreams,
You dreamers,
Bring me all of your
Heart melodies
5 That I may wrap them
In a blue cloud-cloth
Away from the too-rough fingers
Of the world. ❧

SECOND READ

Analyze Literature
Speaker The poem's speaker directly addresses the reader. Why do you think Hughes wrote the poem that way?

FIRST READ

Use Reading Skills
Reread What type of dreams do you think Hughes is referring to? Why?

FIRST READ

Make Connections
How can you keep your dreams safe from "the too-rough fingers of the world"?

Mirrors & Windows

What types of "dreams" are most important to you? If Langston Hughes were alive and invited to speak at a middle school assembly, what advice do you think he would give students about their dreams?

_____

_____

_____

_____

Close Reading Model
AFTER READING

Find Meaning	Make Judgments
1. (a) What is another phrase Hughes uses in the poem to mean *dreams?* (b) Why is this a good description of dreams?	**4.** (a) What effect do you think Hughes wanted this poem to have on readers? (b) How successful do you think he was in achieving that effect?
2. (a) What does the image of a "blue cloud-cloth" bring to mind? (b) What does the imagery tell you about the speaker's feelings about dreams?	**5.** Based on what you learned in the Meet the Author section, how do you think the ideas in this poem might have helped Hughes throughout his own life?
3. (a) What do you think the speaker thinks of sharing dreams? (b) What clue in the poem supports your response?	

Analyze Literature
Speaker Who might the **speaker** of the poem be? Brainstorm possible responses and place them on a cluster chart. Then decide which of the speakers you have identified would make the poem most meaningful for you and explain why.

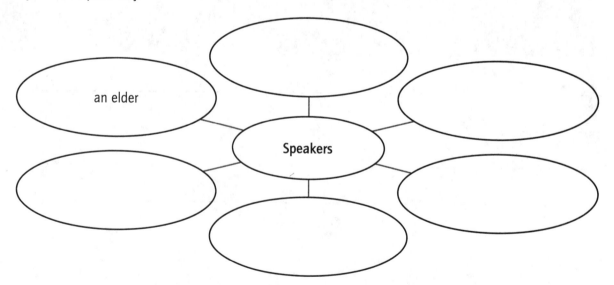

Writing Connection
Explanatory Writing Hughes wrote "The Dream Keeper" from a first-person perspective. How do you think the poem's message and tone would be different had it been written in the third-person point of view? Write Hughes a **letter** explaining how the effect of his poem would differ had he used the third-person point of view.

Close Reading   © Carnegie Learning, Inc.

 page 412

LYRIC POEM by E. E. Cummings

Build Background

Literary Context E. E. Cummings developed a unique style and broke many traditional rules in his poetry. He made up words and used unconventional spelling, punctuation, grammar, and capitalization, even spelling his own name in all lowercase letters—e. e. cummings. Because he was a painter as well as a poet, he approached the writing of poems visually as well as verbally. For instance, he often used gaps between words or scattered words across a page to create certain effects.

Reader's Context Which of the four seasons is your favorite? What do you like best about that season?

_____

_____

Set Purpose

Previewing the first few lines of "in Just-" will show you that the poem uses images and sensory details to describe the season of spring. Read to discover what happens.

Use Reading Skills

Monitor Comprehension Use a chart to monitor your comprehension of "in Just-" as you read. Pause after every few lines to ask yourself, "What is happening here? What does this mean?" In a chart like the one below, write words or lines from the poem that seem confusing or unclear to you. Reread parts or all of the poem to clarify, and write down your understanding.

Words from the Poem	My Understanding
"the world is mud-luscious"	The speaker likes that the ground is muddy in spring.

Analyze Literature

Symbol A **symbol** is a thing that stands for or represents both itself and something else. Some traditional symbols include doves for peace, roses for beauty, winter or evening for old age, and roads or paths for the journey through life.

A Lyric Poem by E. E. Cummings

in Just–

in Just-
spring   when the world is mud-
luscious the little
lame balloonman

5 whistles   far
        and wee

and eddieandbill come
running from marbles and
piracies and it's
10 spring

when the world is puddle-wonderful

the queer
old balloonman whistles
far   and   wee
15 and bettyandisbel come dancing

from hop-scotch and jump-rope and

it's
spring
and
20   the
            goat-footed

balloonMan   whistles
far
and
25 wee ❧

Mirrors & Windows

What words, images, or sensory details would you use to describe spring? How would you describe spring to someone who has never experienced it?

Find Meaning	Make Judgments
1. (a) How does the poet describe the world in "Just-spring"? (b) Why do you think he chose these terms to describe spring?	**4.** (a) How do the people in the poem react to the arrival of spring? (b) How well does "in Just-" describe how the world feels when spring comes?
2. (a) In "in Just-," what do "eddieandbill" do? What do "bettyandisbel" do? (b) How do their activities help show that it is "Just-spring"?	**5.** How does spring cause the people in the poem to act differently than they do in winter?
3. (a) What does the balloonman do in this poem? (b) Why do you think he does this?	

Analyze Literature

Symbol A symbol is a thing that stands for or represents both itself and something else. Why do you think the balloonman whistles "far and wee"? How do the children respond to his whistle? What do you think the balloonman symbolizes? What do you think the season of spring symbolizes in this poem and why?

_____

_____

_____

_____

Writing Connection

Informative Writing Write a **critical analysis** of "in Just-," addressing the use of symbolism, repetition, and form. How does each element affect the meaning of the poem? How does each enhance the mood or sound of the poem? In your opinion, how does the poet's use of these literary elements enhance the overall meaning or sound of the poem? In your analysis, state your opinion in a thesis statement and support it with details and examples from the poem. Share your critical analysis with the class.

Drama Close Reading Model

Key Ideas and Details – What the text says

Build Background

You need to apply two types of background to read a drama effectively. One type is the drama's literary and historical context. The other type of background is the personal knowledge and experience you bring to your reading.

Set Purpose

A playwright presents characters and scenes to say something about life. Set your reading purpose to decide what you want to get out of the drama. Ask yourself questions such as: "What do I know about the setting of the drama and characters?" "What do I want to know more about?"

Make Connections

Notice where connections can be made between the drama and your life or the world outside the drama. What feelings or thoughts do you have while reading the drama?

Use Reading Skills

Apply close reading skills such as making inferences, drawing conclusions, and summarizing. Identify a graphic organizer that will help you apply the skill before and while you read. Make predictions, using dramatic features and structures, about what's going to happen next. When understanding breaks down, reread any difficult parts to increase comprehension.

SECOND READING Craft and Structure – How the text says it

Use Text Organization

Plays are usually divided into acts and scenes, with each scene change indicating a variation of time or place. Stop at the end of scenes or acts and summarize the action that takes place.

What do you learn about the setting, characters, and plot through dialogue spoken by the actors, their actions, or details in the stage directions? As you read, gather more clues to confirm or adjust your predictions.

Analyze Literature

A playwright uses literary techniques, such as plot and dialogue, to create meaning. What literary elements stand out? Are the characters vivid and interesting? Is there a strong central conflict? Think about how these elements affect your enjoyment and understanding of the play.

Unpack Vocabulary

What is the effect of the author's vocabulary and the language choices he makes? Make sure to use the context clues, definitions, and footnotes to help you unpack the language.

THIRD READING Integration of Knowledge and Ideas – What the text means

Find Meaning

Reread to recall the important details of the drama, such as the sequence of events and characters' names. Ask questions about the text, using the information to interpret, or explain, the meaning of the drama.

Make Judgments

- Analyze the text by examining details and deciding what they contribute to the meaning.
- Evaluate the text by making judgments about how the author creates meaning.

Analyze Literature

Review how the use of literary elements increases your understanding of the story. For example, if the author uses monologue, how does it help to shape the drama's meaning?

Extend Understanding

Synthesize information from the text to create new understanding. Go beyond the text by exploring the drama's ideas through writing, discussion, or other collaborative projects.

Unit 7

In the Fog page 469
SCREENPLAY by Milton Geiger

Build Background
Literary Context Today you turn on your television to enjoy a sitcom. Until the 1950s, however, people had to turn on their radios. Listeners tuned in not only to sitcoms but also to radio plays, adventure serials, and children's shows. Radio programs were written by people such as Milton Geiger who specialized in radio drama. Geiger later turned to writing screenplays, such as "In the Fog."

Reader's Context When have you been in a situation that made you feel like something wasn't quite right? What gave you the feeling? How did the situation turn out?

_____

_____

Set Purpose
Look at the title of the screenplay and the illustration. Predict what the mood of the story may be and what might happen.

Use Reading Skills
Draw Conclusions Drawing conclusions helps you put together information you read and determine what it means. As you read, use evidence from the story to draw conclusions about what is happening. Think about what in the story leads you to a particular conclusion. Use an organizer to track your conclusions and the evidence you used to form them.

Text Evidence	Conclusions
The doctor is lost, and it's foggy out.	The doctor is going to encounter some sort of trouble.

> ### Analyze Literature
> **Drama** A **drama** is a story told through characters and **dialogue,** or conversation between characters. Drama is meant to be read or performed by actors before an audience. The experience of a drama includes everything that the audience sees and hears, such as lighting, costumes, props, set pieces, music, sound effects, and the movements and expressions of the actors.

Close Reading

A Screenplay by Milton Geiger

In the Fog

CHARACTERS

THE Doctor

ZEKE

EBEN

FILLING Station Attendant

SETS: *A signpost on Pennsylvania Route 30.*
A rock or stump in the fog. A gas station pump.

FADE IN: *Exterior. Night. At first we can only see fog drifting across a dark scene devoid of detail. Then, to weird minor music, the camera dollies in slowly so that out of the fog there emerges toward us a white roadside signpost with a number of white painted signboards pointing to right and to left. The camera continues to dolly in until it has in closeup the state route marker fastened below the signs on the post. The marker is a Pennsylvania State Route—marked characteristically "PENNA-30." Now, a light as from a far headlight sweeps the signs.*

SOUND: *Automobile approaching on road. The car pulls up close. We hear the car door open and slam and a man's footsteps approaching on the concrete. Now the signs are lit up again by a more localized, smaller source of light. The light grows stronger as the man, off-stage, approaches. The DOCTOR enters the shot, holding a flashlight before him. He* <u>scrutinizes</u> *the road marker. He flashes his light up at the arrows, the camera moving up with the light. We see the legends on the markers. Pointing off right there are markers that read: York, Columbia, Lancaster; pointing left the signs read: Fayetteville, McConnellsburg, Pennsylvania Turnpike.*

CUT TO: *Another angle. We shoot into the DOCTOR's perplexed and annoyed face as he turns his flashlight on a folded road map. He is a bit lost in the fog. Then his flashlight fails him. It goes out!*

DOCTOR. Darn! [*He fumbles with the flashlight in the gloom. Then a voice is raised to him from off-scene.*]

scru‧ti‧nize (skrü´ tən īze')
v., examine something carefully

Close Reading

EBEN. [*Off-scene, strangely.*] Turn around, mister...[*The* DOCTOR *turns sharply to stare off-scene. His face is lit by a bobbing light from off-scene.*]

5   **ZEKE.** [*Off-scene.*] You don't have to be afraid, mister...

CUT TO: *What* DOCTOR *sees. Two men are slowly approaching out of the fog,* grotesque *in the distorting gloom. One carries a lantern below his knees. The other holds a heavy rifle of dim manufacture. Their features are utterly indistinct as they approach and the rifleman holds up his gun with quiet threat.*

CUT TO: *Group shot, angling past* DOCTOR's *shoulder, at their faces.*

EBEN. You don't have to be afraid.

DOCTOR. [*More* indignant *than afraid.*] So you say! Who are you, man?

EBEN. We don't aim to hurt you none.

10 **DOCTOR.** That's reassuring. I'd like to know just what you mean by this? This gun business! Who are you?

ZEKE. [*Mildly.*] What's your trade, mister?

DOCTOR. I...I'm a doctor. Why?

ZEKE. [*To* EBEN.] Doctor.

15 **EBEN.** [*Nods; then to* DOCTOR.] Yer the man we want.

ZEKE. Ye'll do proper, we're thinkin'.

EBEN. So ye'd better come along, mister.

ZEKE. Aye.

DOCTOR. Why? Has—anyone been hurt?

20 **EBEN.** It's for you to say if he's been hurt nigh¹ to the finish.

ZEKE. So we're askin' ye to come along, doctor.

CUT TO: *Another angle, favoring Doctor. He looks from one to another in indecision and puzzlement.*

EBEN. In the name o' mercy.

ZEKE. Aye.

DOCTOR. I want you to understand—I'm not afraid of your
25 gun! I'll go to your man all right. Naturally, I'm a doctor. But I demand to know who you are.

ZEKE. [*Patiently.*] Why not? Raise yer lantern, Eben....

---

1. **nigh.** Almost

gro•tesque (grō tesk´) *adj.*, strangely distorted in a way that is upsetting

in•dig•nant (in dig´ nənt) *adj.*, angry about something that is unfair or unreasonable

FIRST READ

Use Reading Skills
Make Predictions Why do the men want the doctor to come with them?

EBEN. [*Tiredly.*] Aye.

EBEN *lifts his lantern. Its light falls on their faces now and we see that they are terrifying. Matted beards, clotted with blood; crude head bandages, crusty with dirt and dry blood. Their hair, stringy and disheveled. Their faces are lean and hollow-cheeked; their eyes sunken and tragic. The* DOCTOR *is shocked for a moment—then bursts out—*

DOCTOR. Good Lord!—

30 ZEKE. [*Impassively.*] That's Eben, I'm Zeke.

DOCTOR. What's happened? Has there been an accident or... what?

ZEKE. Mischief's happened, stranger.

35 EBEN. Mischief enough.

DOCTOR. [*Looks at the rifle at his chest.*] There's been gunplay—hasn't there?

ZEKE. [*Mildly ironic.²*] Yer tellin' us there's been gunplay!

40 DOCTOR. And I'm telling you that I'm not at all frightened! It's my duty to report this and report it I will!

ZEKE. Aye, mister. You *do* that.

DOCTOR. You're <u>arrogant</u> about it now! You don't think you'll be caught and dealt with. But people are losing patience with

45 you men....

CUT TO: *Close two-shot.* ZEKE and EBEN.

DOCTOR'S VOICE. [*Off-scene.*]...You...you moonshiners!³ Running wild...a law unto yourselves...shooting up the countryside!

50 ZEKE. Hear that, Eben? Moonshiners.

EBEN. Mischief's happened, mister, we'll warrant that...

DOCTOR. And I don't like it!

ZEKE. Can't say we like it better'n you do, mister...

EBEN. [*Strangely sad and remote.*] What must be, must.

55 ZEKE. There's not changin' or goin' back and all 'at's left is the wishin' things were different.

EBEN. Aye.

FIRST READ

Use Reading Skills
Draw Conclusions What does the doctor suspect has happened at this point?

ar•ro•gant (er´ ə gənt) *adj.*, overly confident in a way that annoys others

---

2. **ironic.** Opposite of what is expected
3. **moonshiners.** People who make and sell whiskey illegally

Close Reading © Carnegie Learning, Inc.

DOCTOR. And while we talk your wounded man lies bleeding I suppose—worthless though he may be. Well? I'll have to get
60 my instrument bag, you know. [*Nods off-scene.*] It's in the car.

EBEN *and* ZEKE *part to let* DOCTOR *pass between them.* DOCTOR *leaves shot grimly as they watch him, off-scene.*

SOUND: *Car door opens off-scene. Pause. Slams.*

THE DOCTOR *re-enters the shot, carrying his medical bag.*

DOCTOR. I'm ready. Lead the way.

EBEN *lifts his lantern a bit and goes first.* ZEKE *prods the* DOCTOR *ever so gently and apologetically but firmly with the rifle muzzle. The* DOCTOR *leaves the shot next.* ZEKE *strides off slowly after them.*

DISSOLVE TO: *Exterior, night. Medium shot of a wounded man lying against a section of stone fence or a boulder or a tree trunk. He, too, is bearded though very young and wears some sort of unidentifiable tunic like the other men. His shirt is dark with blood. He breathes stertorously[4] but never stirs otherwise. The light of* EBEN's *bull's-eye[5] falls on him, bobbingly.* EBEN *enters the shot followed by the* DOCTOR *and* ZEKE.

SOUND: *Owl, far off, from time to time.*

ZEKE. Ain't stirred a mite since we left 'im.

DOCTOR. Let's have that lantern here! [*The* DOCTOR *tears the man's shirt for better access to the wound.*]

CLOSE UP: *Doctor's face. Appalled.*

65 **DOCTOR.** [*Softly.*] Dreadful! Dreadful!...

ZEKE'S VOICE. [*Off-scene.*] Reckon it's bad in the chest like that, hey?

DOCTOR. [*Taking pulse.*] His pulse is positively racing!...

TIGHT *group shot.*

DOCTOR. How long has he been this way?

70 **ZEKE.** A long time, mister. A long time....

DOCTOR. [*To* EBEN.] You! Hand me my bag.

EBEN *puts down lantern and hands bag to* DOCTOR. *The* DOCTOR *opens bag and takes out a couple of retractors.[6]* ZEKE *holds lantern close now.*

---

4. **stertorously.** With loud, raspy, difficult breathing
5. **bull's-eye.** Type of lantern
6. **retractors.** Tools used in surgery to pull back skin or an organ

Use Reading Skills
Draw Conclusions In what time period is this drama set? What clues support your response?

Analyze Literature
Drama What does this stage direction reveal about Zeke?

DOCTOR. Lend me a hand with these retractors. [*He works on man, hiding wound from camera with his body.*] All right... when I tell you to draw back on the retractors—draw back.

EBEN. Aye.

75 **ZEKE.** How is 'e, mister?

DOCTOR. [*Preoccupied.*] More retraction. Pull them a bit more. Hold it....

EBEN. Bad, ain't he?

DOCTOR. Bad enough. The bullet didn't touch any lung tissue
80 far as I can see right now. There's some pneumothorax[7] though. All I can do now is plug the wound. There's some cotton and gauze wadding in my bag. Find it....

ZEKE probes about silently in the bag and comes up with a small dark box of gauze.

DOCTOR. That's it. [*Works a moment in silence.*] I've never seen anything quite like it.

85 **EBEN.** Yer young, doctor. Lots o' things you've never seen.

DOCTOR. Adhesive tape!

ZEKE finds a roll of three-inch tape and hands it to the DOCTOR who tears off strips and, unseen to camera, slaps them on the dressing[8] and pats and smooths them to the man's chest. EBEN replaces equipment in DOCTOR's bag and closes it with a hint of the finality to come. A preview of <u>dismissal</u> so to speak.

DOCTOR. [*At length.*] There. So much for that. Now then— [*Takes man's shoulders.*] Give me a hand here.

ZEKE. [*Quiet suspicion.*] What fer?

DOCTOR. We've got to move this man.

90 **ZEKE.** What fer?

DOCTOR. [*Stands; indignantly.*] We've got to get him to a hospital for treatment; a thorough cleansing of the wound; irrigation.[9] I've done all I can for him here.

ZEKE. I reckon he'll be all right, 'thout[10] no hospital.

95 **DOCTOR.** Do you realize how badly this man's hurt!

EBEN. He won't bleed to death, will he?

dis·mis·sal (dis miʹ səl) *n.*, act of sending someone away

---

7. **pneumothorax.** Presence of air in the chest due to a puncture of the lungs
8. **dressing.** Bandages put on a wound
9. **irrigation.** Washing out a wound
10. **'thout.** Without

Close Reading

DOCTOR. I don't think so—not with that plug and the pressure dressing. But bleeding isn't the only danger we've got to—

ZEKE. [*Interrupts.*] All right, then. Much obliged to you.

100 **DOCTOR.** This man's dangerously hurt!

ZEKE. Reckon he'll pull through now, thanks to you.

DOCTOR. I'm glad you feel that way about it! But I'm going to report this to the Pennsylvania State Police at the first telephone I reach!

105 **ZEKE.** We ain't stoppin' ye, mister.

EBEN. Fog is liftin', Zeke. Better be done with this, I say.

ZEKE. [*Nods, sadly.*] Aye. Ye can go now, mister...and thanks.

Group shot. Another angle, favoring ZEKE, *then* EBEN.

ZEKE. [*Continues.*] We never meant a mite o' harm, I can tell ye. If we killed, it was no wish of ours.

110 **EBEN.** What's done is done. Aye.

EBEN. Ye can go now, stranger....

EBEN *hands* ZEKE *the* DOCTOR's *bag.* ZEKE *hands it gently to the* DOCTOR.

DOCTOR. Very well. You haven't heard the last of this, though!

ZEKE. That's the truth, mister. We've killed, aye; and we've been hurt for it....

115 **EBEN.** Hurt bad.

Group shot. Another angle, favoring DOCTOR *in close shot. His face puckered with doubt and strange apprehension.*

FIRST READ

Use Reading Skills
Make Predictions Why do you think Eben and Zeke are resisting taking the wounded man to a hospital?

SECOND READ

Analyze Literature
Drama What does this portion of dialogue lead you to believe about the role of Eben and Zeke in the man's injury?

ZEKE. We're not alone, mister. We ain't the only ones. [*Sighs.*] Ye can go now, doctor...and our thanks to ye....

The camera moves with the DOCTOR *as he leaves the other two, still gazing at them in strange enchantment and wonder and a touch of indignation. Camera takes his body from waist up as he walks against neutral, featureless background wreathed with some tendrils of fog.*

EBEN'S VOICE. [*Off-scene.*] Thanks, mister....

ZEKE'S VOICE. In the name o' mercy...We thank you....

CUT TO: *Close up:* ZEKE *and* EBEN, *their faces grizzled like the faces of monuments in the park in winter; their eyes unhappy and suffering. The fog drifting across them.*

120 EBEN. In the name o' mercy.

ZEKE. Thanks, mister....

EBEN. In the name o' kindness....

The camera pulls back for a group shot of the two men standing; their wounded comrade at their feet—like a group statue in the park...grizzled and time-worn. The fog thickens across the scene.

MUSIC: *Eerie, sad.*

SOUND: *Far off the long, sad wail of a locomotive whimpers in the dark. Then fades.*

FADE OUT.

FADE IN: *The illuminated translucent glass globe atop a gasoline pump. The camera pulls back to show the young Attendant standing in front of the pump taking a reading and recording it in a book as he prepares to close up. Lights sweep him. He turns as he hears the car approach on the gravel drive.*

SOUND: *Car approaching. Crunches on gravel and stops. Door opens and slams shut.* DOCTOR'S *feet crunch on gravel, approaching swiftly.*

DOCTOR *enters shot.*

ATTENDANT. [*Pleasantly.*] Good evening, sir. [*Nods off at off-scene car.*] Care to pull 'er up to this pump, sir? Closing up.

125 DOCTOR. [*Impatiently.*] No. Where's your telephone, please? I've just been held up!

ATTENDANT. Pay-station inside, sir....

DOCTOR. Thank you! [*The* DOCTOR *starts to go past the Attendant.*]

SECOND READ

Analyze Literature
Drama What effect does this stage direction have on you?

Close Reading

130   **ATTENDANT.** Excuse me, sir....

DOCTOR. [*Stops.*] Eh, what is it, what is it?

ATTENDANT. Uh...what sort of looking fellows were they?

DOCTOR. Oh...two big fellows with a rifle; faces and heads bandaged and smeared with dirt and blood. Friend of theirs
135   with a gaping hole in his chest. I'm a doctor so they forced me to attend to him. Why?

ATTENDANT. Those fellers, huh?

DOCTOR. Then you know about them!

ATTENDANT. I guess so.

140   **DOCTOR.** They're armed and they're desperate!

ATTENDANT. That was about two or three miles back, would you say?

DOCTOR. [*Fumbling in pocket.*] Just about—I don't seem to have the change. I wonder if you'd spare me change for a
145   quarter?...

ATTENDANT. [*Makes change from metal coin canister at his belt.*] Certainly, sir....

DOCTOR. What town was that back there, now?

ATTENDANT. [*Dumps coins in other's hand.*] There you are, sir.

150   **DOCTOR.** [*Impatient.*] Yes, thank you. I say—what town was that back there, so I can tell the police?

Two shot. A new angle favoring ATTENDANT. *His eyes are serious and candid; matter-of-fact and very steady.*

ATTENDANT. That was...Gettysburg, mister....

MUSIC: *Softly, eerily poignant.* "Dixie"[11] *and* "Battle Hymn of the Republic"[12] *in minor counterpoint.*

Camera slowly trucks around for two-shot that slowly favors DOCTOR.

DOCTOR. Gettysburg?...

ATTENDANT. Gettysburg and Gettysburg battlefield... [*Looks*
155   *off.*] When it's light and the fog's gone, you can see the gravestones. Meade's men...Pickett's men, Robert E. Lee's....

The DOCTOR *is looking off with the* ATTENDANT; *now he turns his head slowly to stare at the other man.*

---

11. **Dixie.** Marching song associated with Confederate soldiers during the Civil War
12. **Battle Hymn of the Republic.** Song associated with Union soldiers during the Civil War

NOTES

FIRST READ

Use Reading Skills
Draw Conclusions Why might the attendant not be surprised by the doctor's description?

SECOND READ

Analyze Literature
Drama What is the purpose of this choice of music at this point in the screenplay?

ATTENDANT. [*Continues.*] On nights like this—well—you're not the first those men've stopped...or the last. [*Nods off.*] Fill 'er up, mister?

Camera dollies in slowly on the rapt face of the DOCTOR.

160 **DOCTOR.** Yes, fill 'er up....

FADE OUT.

MUSIC FINISHES. ♣

Mirrors & Windows

If you had been the doctor, how might the experience at Gettysburg have affected you? What might be the value in experiencing something frightening or unsettling?

Find Meaning	Make Judgments
1. What does Eben's remark "It's for you to say if he's been hurt nigh to the finish" mean?	**4.** (a) How did the doctor initially respond to Eben and Zeke? (b) Do you think he was wise? Explain.
2. (a) At first, who did the doctor think Eben and Zeke were? (b) What did he think had happened?	**5.** After reading the screenplay, what is your opinion of why Eben and Zeke resisted taking the wounded man to the hospital?
3. (a) What does the doctor do at the end of the play? (b) How do you interpret his action?	**6.** What kind of man do you think the doctor was? Why?

Analyze Literature

Drama A drama, such as "In the Fog," uses dialogue, costumes, props, music, and stage directions to set a mood and unfold the plot or key events. Skim "In the Fog" and use a chart to comment on how each of these elements contributes to the screenplay. Use your chart to summarize how Geiger uses the elements of drama in this selection.

Element	Mood	Plot
Dialogue		
Costumes		"unidentifiable tunic" hints at a Civil War connection
Props		
Music		
Stage Directions		

Writing Connection

Informative Writing Imagine that Milton Geiger is still alive. Write an **analysis** of the ending of the screenplay addressed to him. Tell Geiger whether the ending of the play surprised you. Trace for him the predictions you made and revised as you read the screenplay. Explain what clues led you to make those predictions. Comment on whether you found the ending satisfying or not, and explain why.

Close Reading

Folk Literature Close Reading Model

Key Ideas and Details – What the text says

Build Background

Apply two types of background to read myths, fables, and folk tales effectively. One type is the story's literary and cultural context. The other type of background is the personal knowledge and experience you bring to your reading.

Set Purpose

Folk literature presents characters and actions to say something about life. Set your purpose for reading to decide what you want to get out of the story. Ask yourself questions such as: "What do I know about the setting of the tale and the characters?" "What do I want to know more about?"

Make Connections

Notice where connections can be made between the story and your life or another story, myth, or legend. What feelings or thoughts do you have while reading the story?

Use Reading Skills

Use Reading Skills, such as identifying the main idea, analyzing cause and effect, and making inferences, to help you get the most out of your reading. Make predictions, using text features and structures, about what's going to happen next. Identify a graphic organizer to help you apply the skill before and while you read.

SECOND READING Craft and Structure – How the text says it

Use Text Organization

- Break the text down or "chunk" the text into smaller sections to check your comprehension.
- Stop at the end of paragraphs or sections to summarize what you have read. Reread any difficult parts.
- As you read, gather more clues to confirm or adjust your predictions.

Analyze Literature

Folk literature includes literary techniques, such as plot and setting, to create meaning. What literary elements stand out? Are the characters vivid and interesting? Is there a lesson or moral? Monitor your comprehension as you read, considering how these elements affect your enjoyment and understanding of the story.

Unpack Language

What is the effect of the author's vocabulary and the language choices he or she makes? Make sure to use margin definitions, footnotes, and context clues that give hints to the meaning.

THIRD READING Integration of Knowledge and Ideas – What the text means

Find Meaning

Reread to recall the important details of the story, such as the sequence of events and character traits. Ask questions about the text, using the information to help interpret, or explain, the meaning.

Make Judgments

- Analyze the text by examining details and deciding what they contribute to the meaning.
- Evaluate the text by making judgments about how the author creates meaning.

Analyze Literature

Review how the use of literary elements increases your understanding of the story. For example, if the story includes dialogue, how does it help shape the story's meaning?

Extend Understanding

Synthesize information from the text to create new understanding. Go beyond the text by exploring the story through writing, discussion, or other collaborative projects.

Unit 8

ARACHNE page 515

GREEK MYTH retold by Olivia Coolidge

Build Background

Cultural Context Greek mythology includes many stories about the gods, their actions on Earth, and their relationships with the human beings who please or anger them. Zeus, god of thunder and the sky, was king of the gods. The myth of Arachne introduces his daughter Athene, the goddess of wisdom. She was also a goddess of crafts like spinning and weaving. According to myth, Arachne lived in the country of Lydia, famous for its beautiful woven goods.

Reader's Context Have you ever watched a spider spinning its web? What did the spider's web remind you of?

_____

_____

Analyze Literature

Myth A **myth** is a traditional story that usually presents supernatural events involving gods and heroes. An **origin myth** is a story that explains objects or events in the natural world. Reading myths can help you better understand the cultures that produced them. As you read, think about what important beliefs or values are expressed in this myth.

Set Purpose

Preview the Cultural Context. As you read, make inferences to predict whether Arachne's words and actions will please or anger Athene.

Use Reading Skills

Analyze Cause and Effect A cause can have multiple effects, and an effect can have multiple causes. As you read, determine what cause or causes occur in "Arachne" and the effect or effects they produce. In a chart like the one below, record the causes and the effects.

Cause(s)	Effect(s)
	Arachne is famous across Greece for her spinning and weaving.

A Greek Myth retold by Olivia Coolidge

ARACHNE

ob·scure (äb skyùr´) *adj.*, remote; not well known

1   Arachne[1] was a maiden who became famous throughout Greece, though she was neither wellborn[2] nor beautiful and came from no great city. She lived in an <u>obscure</u> little village, and her father was a humble dyer of wool. In this he was very skillful, producing many varied shades, while above all he was famous for the clear, bright scarlet which is made from shellfish, and which was the most glorious of all the colors used in ancient Greece. Even more skillful than her father was Arachne. It was her task to spin the fleecy wool into a fine, soft thread and to weave it into cloth on the high, standing loom within the cottage. Arachne was small and pale from much working. Her eyes were light and her hair was a dusty brown, yet she was quick and graceful, and her fingers, roughened as they were, went so fast that it was hard to follow their flickering movements. So soft and even was her thread, so fine her cloth, so gorgeous her embroidery,[3] that soon her products were known all over Greece. No one had ever seen the like of them before.

2   At last Arachne's fame became so great that people used to come from far and wide to watch her working. Even the graceful nymphs would steal in from stream or forest and peep shyly through the dark doorway, watching in wonder the white arms of Arachne as she stood at the loom and threw the shuttle from hand to hand between the hanging threads, or drew out the long wool, fine as a hair, from the distaff[4] as she sat spinning. "Surely Athene herself must have taught her," people would murmur to one another. "Who else could know the secret of such marvelous skill?"

3   Arachne was used to being wondered at, and she was immensely proud of the skill that had brought so many to look on her. Praise was all she lived for, and it displeased her greatly that people should think anyone, even a goddess, could teach her anything. Therefore when she heard them murmur, she would stop her work and turn round indignantly to say, "With my own ten fingers I gained this skill, and by hard

SECOND READ

Analyze Literature
Myth How did the people watching think Arachne gained her skill?

---

1. **Arachne.** Greek word for *spider*
2. **wellborn.** Of noble birth
3. **embroidery.** Decoration made on fabric with a needle and thread
4. **distaff.** Short rod for holding the wool in spinning

practice from early morning till night. I never had time to stand looking as you people do while another maiden worked. Nor if I had, would I give Athene credit because the girl was more skillful than I. As for Athene's weaving, how could there be finer cloth or more beautiful embroidery than mine? If Athene herself were to come down and compete with me, she could do no better than I."

4   One day when Arachne turned round with such words, an old woman answered her, a grey old woman, bent and very poor, who stood leaning on a staff and peering at Arachne amid the crowd of onlookers. "Reckless girl," she said, "how dare you claim to be equal to the immortal[5] gods themselves? I am an old woman and have seen much. Take my advice and ask pardon of Athene for your words. Rest content with your fame of being the best spinner and weaver that <u>mortal</u> eyes have ever beheld."

5   "Stupid old woman," said Arachne indignantly, "who gave you a right to speak in this way to me? It is easy to see that you were never good for anything in your day, or you would not come here in poverty and rags to gaze at my skill. If Athene resents my words, let her answer them herself. I have challenged her to a contest, but she, of course, will not come. It is easy for the gods to avoid matching their skill with that of men."

6   At these words the old woman threw down her staff and stood erect. The wondering onlookers saw her grow tall and fair and stand clad in long robes of dazzling white. They were terribly afraid as they realized that they stood in the presence of Athene. Arachne herself flushed red for a moment, for she had never really believed that the goddess would hear her. Before the group that was gathered there she would not give in; so pressing her pale lips together in <u>obstinacy</u> and pride, she led the goddess to one of the great looms and set herself before the other. Without a word both began to thread the long woolen strands that hang from the rollers, and between which the shuttle moves back and forth. Many skeins lay heaped beside them to use, bleached white, and gold, and scarlet, and other shades, varied as the rainbow. Arachne had never thought of giving credit for her success to her father's skill in dyeing, though in actual truth the colors were as remarkable as the cloth itself.

5. immortal. Living forever

SECOND READ

Analyze Literature
Myth What is Arachne claiming about her skill compared to Athene's skill?

SECOND READ

Analyze Literature
Myth Why does the old woman object to Arachne's words?

mor•tal (môr´ t[ə]l) *adj.,* human

ob•sti•na•cy (äb´ stə nə sē) *n.,* determination to follow a course of action in spite of reason or persuasion

7   Soon there was no sound in the room but the breathing of the onlookers, the whirring of the shuttles, and the creaking of the wooden frames as each pressed the thread up into place or tightened the pegs by which the whole was held straight. The excited crowd in the doorway began to see that the skill of both in truth was very nearly equal, but that, however the cloth might turn out, the goddess was the quicker of the two. A pattern of many pictures was growing on her loom. There was a border of twined branches of the olive, Athene's favorite tree, while in the middle, figures began to appear. As they looked at the glowing colors, the spectators realized that Athene was weaving into her pattern a last warning to Arachne. The central figure was the goddess herself competing with Poseidon[6] for possession of the city of Athens; but in the four corners were mortals who had tried to strive with gods and pictures of the awful <u>fate</u> that had overtaken them. The goddess ended a little before Arachne and stood back from her marvelous work to see what the maiden was doing.

fate (fāt) *n.*, outcome that is impossible to change or escape from

8   Never before had Arachne been matched against anyone whose skill was equal, or even nearly equal to her own. As she stole glances from time to time at Athene and saw the goddess working swiftly, calmly, and always a little faster than herself, she became angry instead of frightened, and an evil thought came into her head. Thus as Athene stepped back a pace to watch Arachne finishing her work, she saw that the maiden had taken for her design a pattern of scenes which showed

6. Poseidon. Greek god of the sea

evil or unworthy actions of the gods, how they had deceived fair maidens, resorted to trickery, and appeared on earth from time to time in the form of poor and humble people. When the goddess saw this insult glowing in bright colors on Arachne's loom, she did not wait while the cloth was judged, but stepped forward, her grey eyes blazing with anger, and tore Arachne's work across. Then she struck Arachne across the face. Arachne stood there a moment, struggling with anger, fear, and pride. "I will not live under this insult," she cried, and seizing a rope from the wall, she made a noose and would have hanged herself.

9   The goddess touched the rope and touched the maiden "Live on, wicked girl," she said. "Live on and spin, both you and your descendants. When men look at you they may remember that it is not wise to <u>strive</u> with Athene." At that the body of Arachne shriveled up[7], and her legs grew tiny, spindly,[8] and distorted. There before the eyes of the spectators hung a little dusty brown spider on a slender thread.

10   All spiders descend from Arachne, and as the Greeks watched them spinning their thread wonderfully fine, they remembered the contest with Athene and thought that it was not right for even the best of men to claim equality with the gods. ✣

---

7. **shriveled up.** Became shrunken and wrinkled
8. **spindly.** Having a long and thin appearance

© Carnegie Learning, Inc.

Close Reading

Mirrors & Windows

Arachne's self-confidence shapes the way she presents herself to others. When have you felt confident in a skill or talent that you possess? How might the possession of an incredible skill or talent affect a young person in today's world?

Find Meaning	**Make Judgments**
1. (a) For what skill does Arachne become famous? (b) What effect does Arachne's skill have on her life?	**4.** (a) How does Arachne respond to other people's suggestions or advice in this myth? (b) What does this say about her character?
2. (a) What does Arachne say about Athene's skill at weaving? (b) Is her opinion of Athene's skill correct? Why or why not?	**5.** Do you think Arachne deserved her fate? Why or why not?
3. Compare and contrast the designs that Athene and Arachne choose for their weavings. How does Athene's design foreshadow what happens to Arachne?	**6.** (a) If you were Arachne, would you have paid attention to the old woman's warning? (b) What would you have done when Athene accepted your challenge?

Analyze Literature

Myth Greek myths express values or beliefs held by the ancient Greeks. What belief about the relationship between gods and humans is expressed in this myth? What statement does Arachne make that shows she does not hold this belief? Use a chart to record your ideas, and cite evidence from the text as support. Based on your ideas and evidence, summarize what was valued in Greek culture, according to this myth. Reflect on and explain how you adjusted your inferences or predictions as new evidence was presented.

Ideas	Evidence
Summary	

Writing Connection

Narrative Writing Write a **narrative paragraph** about a time you engaged in competition, such as in a sporting event, spelling bee, or art contest. Describe who you were competing against, what happened, and how you felt during the competition. What was the outcome? Share your paragraph with the class.

Why Monkeys Live in Trees page 526

WEST AFRICAN FOLK TALE retold by Julius Lester

Build Background

Cultural Context Folk tales exist in every culture across the world. African folk tales often seek to explain the relationship between human beings and nature, using the African environment and featuring animals as main characters. Each of these animal characters represents a single human quality, such as vanity, wit, or cleverness. One common character in African folklore is the trickster. In West Africa, the trickster often takes the form of the spider, but in this folk tale, the trickster is a monkey.

Reader's Context When have you encountered a challenge that could be solved by using your wits? How did you react?

_____

_____

Analyze Literature

Folk tale A **folk tale** is a story in folk literature passed by word of mouth from generation to generation. Folk tales often share a lesson or explanation about the world. As you read "Why Monkeys Live in Trees," think about why a story like this would be passed down from generation to generation. What life lesson does it provide?

Set Purpose

Preview the beginning of the folk tale, and make predictions about the contest and its outcome.

Use Reading Skills

Use Context Clues Preview the vocabulary words from this selection as they are used in the sentences below. Try to unlock the meaning of each word using the context clues provided by the sentences.

1. Sarah caught sight of her <u>reflection</u> in the shop window.

_____

2. The king was very proper and always behaved <u>regally</u>.

_____

3. We all heard Dad <u>bellow</u> with rage when he tripped over my skateboard.

_____

4. The audience was <u>astonished</u> by the acrobat's height.

_____

5. Making sure the chair was <u>sturdy</u>, Mike climbed on top of it to reach the top cabinet

_____

re·flec·tion (ri flek´ shən) *n.*, production of an image by, or as if by, a mirror

FIRST READ

Use Reading Skills
Make Inferences What do these details tell you about Leopard's character?

re·gal·ly (rē´ gə lē) *adv.*, in a royal fashion; in a kingly or queenly manner

SECOND READ

Analyze Literature
Folk Tale What does the inclusion of these different animals tell you about the culture this story comes from?

A West African Folk Tale retold by Julius Lester

Why Monkeys Live in Trees

1   One day Leopard was looking for his <u>reflection</u> in a pool of water. Looking at himself was Leopard's favorite thing in the world to do. Leopard gazed,[1] wanting to be sure that every hair was straight and that all his spots were where they were supposed to be. This took many hours of looking at his reflection, which Leopard did not mind at all.

2   Finally he was satisfied that nothing was disturbing his handsomeness, and he turned away from the pool of water. At that exact moment, one of Leopard's children ran up to him.

3   "Daddy! Daddy! Are you going to be in the contest?"

4   "What contest?" Leopard wanted to know. If it was a beauty contest, of course he was going to be in it.

5   "I don't know. Crow the Messenger just flew by. She said that King Gorilla said there was going to be a contest."

6   Without another word, Leopard set off. He went north-by-northeast, made a right turn at the mulberry bush and traveled east-by-south-by-west until he came to a hole in the ground. He went around in a circle five times, and headed north-by-somersault[2] until he came to a big clearing in the middle of the jungle and that's where King Gorilla was.

7   King Gorilla sat at one end of the clearing on his throne. Opposite him, at the other side of the clearing, all the animals sat in a semicircle. In the middle, between King Gorilla and the animals, was a huge mound of what looked like black dust.

8   Leopard looked around with calm dignity. Then he strode <u>regally</u> over to his friend, Lion.

9   "What's that?" he asked, pointing to the mound of black dust.

10   "Don't know," Lion replied. "King Gorilla said he will give a pot of gold to whoever can eat it in one day. I can eat it in an hour."

11   Leopard laughed. "I'll eat it in a half hour."

12   It was Hippopotamus's turn to laugh. "As big as my mouth is, I'll eat that mound in one gulp."

13   The time came for the contest. King Gorilla had the animals pick numbers to see who would go in what order. To everybody's dismay,[3] Hippopotamus drew Number 1.

---

1. **gazed.** Looked steadily with wonder
2. **somersault.** Acrobatic flip in the air
3. **dismay.** Disappointment

14   Hippopotamus walked over to the mound of black dust. It was bigger than he had thought. It was much too big to eat in one gulp. Nonetheless, Hippopotamus opened his mouth as wide as he could, and that was very wide indeed, and took a mouthful of the black dust.

15   He started chewing. Suddenly he leaped straight into the air and screamed. He screamed so loudly that it knocked the ears off the chickens and that's why to this day chickens don't have ears.

16   Hippopotamus screamed and Hippopotamus yelled. Hippopotamus roared and Hippopotamus <u>bellowed</u>. Then he started sneezing and crying and tears rolled down his face like he was standing in the shower. Hippopotamus ran to the river and drank as much water as he could, and that was very much, indeed, to cool his mouth and tongue and throat.

bel·low (be´ lō[']) *v.*, make a loud noise; roar

17   The animals didn't understand what had happened to Hippopotamus, but they didn't care. They were happy because they still had a chance to win the pot of gold. Of course, if they had known that the mound of black dust was really a mound of black pepper, maybe they wouldn't have wanted the gold.

18   Nobody was more happy than Leopard because he had drawn Number 2. He walked up to the black mound and sniffed at it.

19   "AAAAAAAAACHOOOOOOO!" Leopard didn't like that but then he remembered the pot of gold. He opened his mouth wide, took a mouthful and started chewing and swallowing.

20   Leopard leaped straight into the air, did a back double flip and screamed. He yelled and he roared and he bellowed and, finally, he started sneezing and crying, tears rolling down his face like a waterfall. Leopard ran to the river and washed out his mouth and throat and tongue.

21   Lion was next, and the same thing happened to him as it did to all the animals. Finally only Monkey remained.

22   Monkey approached King Gorilla. "I know I can eat all of whatever that is, but after each mouthful, I'll need to lie down in the tall grasses and rest."

23   King Gorilla said that was okay.

24   Monkey went to the mound, took a tiny bit of pepper on his tongue, swallowed, and went into the tall grasses. A few

FIRST READ

Use Reading Skills
Make Predictions How successful do you think Monkey will be?

as•ton•ished (ə stä´ nishd) *adj.*, amazed

stur•dy (stur´ dē) *adj.*, strong; stable

FIRST READ →

Make Connections
How does this discovery affect your feelings about Monkey?

FIRST READ →

Use Reading Skills
Monitor Comprehension What causes Leopard to take action?

---

minutes later, Monkey came out, took a little more, swallowed it, and went into the tall grasses.

25   Soon the pile was almost gone. The animals were <u>astonished</u> to see Monkey doing what they had not been able to do. Leopard couldn't believe it either. He climbed a tree and stretched out on a <u>sturdy</u> limb to get a better view. From his limb high in the tree Leopard could see into the tall grasses where Monkey went to rest. Wait a minute! Leopard thought something was suddenly wrong with his eyes because he thought he saw a hundred monkeys hiding in the tall grasses.

26   He rubbed his eyes and looked another look. There wasn't anything wrong with his eyes. There *were* a hundred monkeys in the tall grasses and they all looked alike!

27   Just then, there was the sound of loud applause. King Gorilla announced that Monkey had won the contest and the pot of gold.

28   Leopard growled a growl so scary that even King Gorilla was frightened. Leopard wasn't thinking about anybody except the monkeys. He took a long and beautiful leap from the tree right smack into the middle of the tall grasses where the monkeys were hiding.

29   The monkeys ran in all directions. When the other animals saw monkeys running from the grasses, they realized that the monkeys had tricked them and starting chasing them. Even King Gorilla joined in the chase. He wanted his gold back.

30   The only way the monkeys could escape was to climb to the very tops of the tallest trees where no one else, not even Leopard, could climb.

31   And that's why monkeys live in trees to this very day. ✤

Mirrors & Windows

Why do you think the author chose the two human characteristics of cleverness and pride to compete against one another? What does the outcome say about human nature?

Find Meaning	Make Judgments
1. (a) Why is Leopard interested in the contest? (b) What does his motivation say about him?	**4.** Besides its explanation for why monkeys live in trees, what other aspect of nature does this folk tale explain?
2. (a) Why do the other animals continue with the contest after seeing what happens to Hippopotamus? (b) How does their decision to continue help Monkey win the gold?	**5.** (a) Do you think King Gorilla knows what the mound of black dust is? (b) If so, why would he offer so much gold to the animal who eats it all?
3. (a) Why does Monkey go into the tall grasses after each bite of black pepper? (b) How does this affect the outcome of the story?	

Analyze Literature

Folk Tale Each character in "Why Monkeys Live in Trees" represents a human quality. Use a chart to note each animal's traits and the human qualities associated with them.

	Animal's Traits	Human Qualities
Leopard	beauty, grace	conceit, pride
Gorilla		
Hippopotamus		
Monkey		

Writing Connection

Descriptive Writing A reader should be able to visualize everything about a character—mannerisms, appearance, style, and so on—through an author's characterization. Choose one character from this folk tale on which to focus a **character study.** Expand on the details from the story to describe your character in depth.